My Big Christmas Book

Written by Hayden McAllister

THIS EDITION PRODUCED BY PETER HADDOCK LTD
FOR CLUNY BOOKS
DISTRIBUTED BY PUBLISHERS DIRECT SALES
UNIT 9, 25 CONNELL COURT, ETOBICOKE, ONTARIO M8ZIE8
© PESTALOZZI VERLAG
PRINTED IN ITALY

$24.95

CONTENTS

At Christmas Time . . .

Every year at Christmas time
You can hear the church bells
    chime.

They ring out on Christmas morn;
For that's the day that Jesus was
    born.

And each year from Heaven above
Your own special Angel brings you
    her love.

The Friends of Santa Claus

An old man with a very long beard
leads a donkey with very big ears,
and four angels in dresses so bright;
follow behind him on Christmas night.

The old man hums as he carries a tree.
The angels sing and dance with glee.
And because they help with Santa's
   chores;
they are known as 'Friends of Santa
   Claus'.

In the middle of the donkey's back
there is tied a bulging sack.
It's full of gifts for girls and boys;
clowns, dolls and clockwork toys.

So if you should see 'Santa's Friends',
sometime before Christmas day
   ends . . .
Give them a smile, a wave or a cheer;
and you'll be Santa's Friend too,
for many a year!

Christmas Verses

Little Robin Redbreast
Sat upon a rail;
Niddle naddle went his head,
Wiggle waggle went his tail.

If Candlemas Day be bright and fair;
Winter will have another flight.
But if on Candlemas Day be shower and rain,
Winter is gone; and won't come again.

God rest you merry gentlemen
Let nothing you dismay;
For Jesus Christ our Saviour
Was born on Christmas Day.

Christmas is coming
The Geese are getting fat.
Please put a penny
In the old man's hat.

I saw three ships go sailing by,
Sailing by; sailing by.
I saw three ships go sailing by,
On Christmas day in the morning.

The Star stopped and stood still.
Right over Bethlehem on the hill.
Over the city of David, where Christ was born —
Stood the brightest star in the grey of morn.

Tomorrow is Christmas Day

An angel tiptoes by.
The coloured candles shine.
The wind begins to sigh;
It's almost Christmas time.

Look!
Skipping in the snow,
The squirrels and rabbits play.
It's almost as if they know —
Tomorrow is Christmas day.

Listen to the Christmas sounds,
As three happy songbirds sing.
While deep within the darkest woods,
Santa's sleigh-bells ring.

A Christmas Alphabet

A   is for ANGEL
B   is for BETHLEHEM where Jesus was born
C   is for Christmas CAROL
D   is for DONKEYS in the stable
       (Where Christ was born)
E   is for lots of EXCITEMENT
F   is for FEASTING
G   is for GOODWILL towards *all* men.
H   is for HOLLY (and)
I   is for IVY
J   is for JOY
K   is for Christ the KING (of love)
L   is for LOVE
M   is for the MANGER where Jesus was born
N   is for NÖEL
O   is for the ORIENT where the Christmas
       Story took place.
P   is for PEACE; just as
Q   is for QUIET
R   is for Santa's REINDEER (and)
S   is for SANTA Claus himself
T   is for The THREE Wise Men
U   is for Once UPON a Time . . .
V   is for the VIRGIN Mother
W   is for Good King WENCESLAS
X   is for XMAS
Y   is for YULETIDE
Z   is for the last letter in the Christmas Alphabet

The Christmas Angels

"Goodness gracious me!"
  Said the keeper of the Christmas keys.
"Now why should I need to remember
  the 24th of December?
Of course!" he cried. "I do believe
  it is the date of Christmas Eve!
Oh dearie me, oh dear.
I forget it every year!"

"I hope it's not too late
for this very important date!"
Said the man with the Christmas keys;
(after sneezing a Christmas sneeze).
He opened wide a golden door
and out the Christmas angels poured!
They wore dresses of pink and white
and carried presents of colours so bright.
What a wonderfully happy sight
to behold on a Christmas night!
A land of dreams and sheer delight,
full of song — laughter and light.
Each year the angels made toys
(for those very special girls and boys
who did no wrong throughout the year).
And no matter where those children were
the angels would take great care,
to bring them angel-blessed dolls;
or books, or clowns, or cakes or play-balls.
But even better than their angel-toys
Were the *blessings* the angels brought
to those good little girls and boys.

Three good children looked into the night
Watching the snow turn everything white.

14

Their names were Allan, John and Jill.
And out beyond their windowsill
They could see the old steeple
And hear the town people
Singing carols on Christmas Eve.

Tomorrow would be Christmas Day
And the children hoped to play.
Already they had a plan
To build a great snowman
At least a metre tall!

"If the snowman is a friend,"
Said Allan, "He might just send
Our sister Sarah a toy.
And bring her some Christmas joy!"
(Sarah was upstairs sleeping)

"We shouldn't worry about toys,"
Said Jill. "Because some girls and boys
Aren't as lucky as we are.
So let's wish on a star
For the happiness of *all* children!"

"Yes!" said Allan. "You're right.
But look! Did you see that light
Flash across the window?
It was ever so bright!
Just like a falling star!"

Now that falling star meant that
Their very own Christmas angel
Had landed in Sarah's room . . .

Sarah was sleeping still
And the angel's light did fill
The room, like a glowing smile.
Then the angel knelt beside the child
And kissed her gently.

Sarah wanted a teddybear for Christmas.
And that's just what she got!
The angel laid it by her cot.
It was as soft as fairy snow,
And its golden colour seemed to glow
Like warm sunshine.

The Christmas angel also left a trainset
(For Allan the older boy
Who liked a clockwork toy).
For Jill the angel brought down
A happy and smiling clown
With a bell on its hat
Which went 'Ding Dong!'
And finally, for little John
The angel left the sparkling
Christmas tree.

And so we leave that happy home
And travel through the snow again.

The angels travelled to lots of places
Visiting children of many races.
They flew as fast as starlight
In their heavenly flight.
And all to make children happy.

They were so very, very swift
That they could leave a special gift
With a lucky child, in a twinkling.
And then be gone in the blinking
Of an eye.

Many a child had a big surprise
When they opened their sleepy eyes
On Christmas morning to see,
That the angels had left two, even three
Lovely presents.

Now when one little girl was brought
A new pen, she thought,
She would write to the angels above;
Sending them her fondest love,
And thanking them for her gift.

And as it was the angels who brought the
    pen.
She could use it to write and thank them!
On Christmas day many girls and boys
Could thank the angels for their toys.
And many of them did!

One little girl who loved drawing,
Was given a gift that sent her heart soaring.
It was a big box of coloured pens;
And these she shared with all her friends.
(Which pleased the angels when they heard!)

One little girl was given a paint-box.
While her brother received some bright new socks.
Another boy was given a story-book.
And his sister, an apron in which to cook
Things like scones and angel-cakes.

Of two twin sisters, one got a broom,
With which she could clean up her room.
While her sister was given a tea-set,
Which she thought her best present yet.
So the twins were doubly happy!

Then there was one poor little girl
(With hardly a friend in the world)
Who didn't expect gifts coming her way.
Yet when she arose on Christmas day,
She found a tree and many parcels bright,
Put there secretly on Christmas night —
By those thoughtful little angels!

After the angels' tasks were done,
They began their long journey home;
Where, for a year they would
    work and play,
Until the following Christmas day
When they would fly again to earth.

Now the keeper of the Christmas keys
Was really rather pleased
To be the angels' special friend.
But he wasn't so keen to spend
Any time alone.

So while the angels were away,
He began to sniff and sneeze
And jangle his bunch of golden keys.
Then he thought he heard a knock,
Which gave him an excuse to unlock
The big golden door.

But there were no angels there.
Only clouds and stars and fresh air.
So finally he sat down in his chair.
Star-dust settled on his silver hair . . .
And he fell asleep.

He dreamed; and the song he heard
Was as if sung by a heavenly bird.
Just like his favourite angel's singing.
Then he heard the door bell ringing!
The angels were back!
The keykeeper cried, "Well, hello!
I thought you'd be back hours ago!"
The angels chorused in reply:
"We've been back an hour or two.
But we didn't want to waken you!"

"Oh, I see!" cried the keeper of the keys.
"Right-ho and dearie me!
Well, now it's time for *you* to rest.
So choose the cloud-pillows you like best."
The angels passed through the golden door
Into a magic world that you'd adore:
Skies as royal blue as the seas.
Sweet smelling scents from tall pine trees.

Animals playing in a soft glow
Of heavenly light and cottonwool snow.
Birds singing and deer nearby.
And the wind sighing a lullaby.
Rabbits, squirrels and
    star-filled space;
Where everything has its
    natural place.

After making sure things were just right
The keykeeper quietly said, "Goodnight!"
Soon the angels became sleepyheads,
As warm in their fleecy cloud beds
They dreamed the night away.

Meanwhile, a million miles away,
On earth, it was still Christmas day.
And a lonely orphan boy and girl
Had just returned from a long walk
In the great snow-filled woods.

So just imagine the great joy
Which was felt by that girl and boy
When they found their home aglow with light.
It was shining from a Christmas tree bright.
And there in the middle of the floor
Was a present they'd both hoped for.

It truly was a miracle!
And it wouldn't have been possible
But for the love of a Christmas angel!

Back in heaven once more.
And right outside the golden door . . .

The keeper of the keys
Had drunk his morning cup of tea.
And he was rather pleased to see
The Christmas angels awake again.
One or two were yawning
Because it was still early morning.
So the keeper of the keys
Whispered very softly: "Please.
What are you going to do today?
Is it to be work — or play?"
"Soon; we'll do some work."
He heard the angels say.
"And then perhaps we'll play.
But *first* we want a song from *you*!"
"Oh me, Oh my! A song from me!"
Cried the keeper of the keys.
"And which song is this?"
"A song from you at Christmas —
For children everywhere!"
Chorused the angel choir.
"A jolly good idea, and I agree!"
Said the keeper of the keys.
"But let's sing it all together.
A one — a two and a three."

WE WISH YOU A MERRY CHRISTMAS
AND A HAPPY NEW YEAR!

In the Christmas Workshop

In the Autumn, when the leaves are falling, you may see lots of stars about. You might even see one special star, twinkling a little more than the rest. Well, inside that bright star is the Christmas Workshop, where the clever fairies work.

Throughout the year, Winter, Spring, Summer or Autumn, the fairies will be there making all kinds of things: toys, clothes, cakes, dolls and teddybears. Imagine any toy you like ... the fairies can make it. And that is why they are known as the 'clever fairies'.

These fairies (really tiny angels who wear white dresses,) gather together on every single night of the year to work in the Christmas Workshop. But in the Autumn, they work harder than ever to get ready for Christmas.

This is the room where all the dolls' and small children's clothes are made. First a fairy cuts the cloth to size, and then passes the pieces to the fairy on the sewing machine. Another fairy sews by hand, and another puts the clothes on the dolls. One fairy makes beautiful bows out of ribbons for some of the clothes.

The Holy Man you can see in the picture has brought some dresses along. They are a present to the clever fairies from the Christmas angels.

Now we are in the heart of the Christmas Workshop, where all the toys are made. Most of the toys are shaped out of wood. The fairies then saw, plane and hammer pieces of wood together to make all types of toys.

They make dolls' houses, cots, sledges, skis, wooden trains, tiny Christmas trees, tanks, spinning tops and toy animals. Once these toys have been nailed or glued together they are painted in many bright colours.

You can almost taste those mouth-watering cooking smells coming from the next room . . . and no wonder, for it's the Christmas Workshop Bakery, where the fairy chefs work. One fairy beats the eggs with her whisk to make some meringues. Another rolls out the pastry while her friend cuts out different shapes with the pastry-cutter.

Across the room is the oven, where scones, tarts and other goodies have been cooking. One fairy is sprinkling caster sugar on to some currant buns. But perhaps the luckiest fairy of all is the one who tastes some of the food after it has been cooked.

This is the room where the cleverest of the clever fairies work. Have you ever wondered what happens to all those toys that children break and then throw away? Well, the clever fairies try and collect as many of these toys as they can; because with care, patience and skill, they can repair broken dolls, clowns and puppets and make them as good as new. If a leg is missing from a doll, they make another one and stitch it back on. If a furry rabbit has lost one of its ears, the clever fairies lovingly make it another ear. It's the same with clowns or teddybears. The clever fairies will rescue, and repair them all . . .

Can you now guess the reason for the work that goes on all the year round at the Christmas Workshop? Of course! It's to make sure that Santa Claus doesn't run out of presents.

Every year the clever fairies from the Christmas Workshop make thousands of lovely toys for boys and girls of all ages. Then on Christmas Eve Santa Claus arrives with his sledge and parks it on a cloud, just outside the Workshop. From there the clever fairies help him to load up with presents, ready for his speedy journey to Earth.

Some of the clever fairies help Santa Claus with his tasks, so they, too, fly through the stars to Earth with their little fairy wings. Just outside the Christmas Workshop the fairies have planted Christmas trees, and on Christmas Eve they decorate the trees with candles, coloured lights, bells and Christmas stars. Then, with a few presents for some lucky children tucked under their arms, the fairies fly off with their lighted Christmas trees — through the magic clouds and down to Earth.

Did you enjoy your peep into the Christmas Workshop?
Come again soon! The clever fairies will always be pleased
   to see you!
Next time you play with your toys you might just wonder if
   they were made in the Christmas Workshop.
Perhaps they were . . .

Christmas Bakery

In Germany and Austria at Christmas time, children help their mothers to bake cakes and biscuits, which they decorate and then use to hang on their Christmas trees.

Some of the biscuits are cut out to the shapes shown on the following pages.

Here is a recipe for:

SPICED BISCUITS

2 eggs
170 g sugar
Pinch ground cloves
Pinch ground cardamom
55 g chopped almonds
42 g chopped candied peel
A little grated lemon rind
55 g ground almonds
1 teasp ground cinnamon
170 g flour

Method: Cream the beaten eggs well with sugar. Add spices and remaining ingredients, stirring in sieved flour last of all.

Roll out thinly, cut into shapes. Bake for 20–25 minutes on a greased baking sheet in moderate oven.

Coat with chocolate or royal icing and coloured sugar. Or pipe with this icing, and decorate with cherries and sweets.

1 egg
60 g icing sugar

Whisk the egg white, then beat in sieved sugar. Beat well together. Put in an icing bag and pipe your design on to the biscuits.

IMPISH BISCUITS

These can be cut out in the shape of imps — or the Christmas star if you wish.

You will need:

500 g sieved flour
200 g sugar
250 g butter or margarine
Teasp vanilla essence
2 eggs
125 g ground hazelnuts
Filling
some marmalade and icing sugar
mixed together

Method : Cream butter and sugar. Add vanilla essence and eggs. Slowly add flour and hazelnuts. Mix well. Place on floured board and put in fridge for 15 minutes. Roll out thinly; cut into shapes and place on greased tray.

Bake for about 15 minutes in moderate oven. When cool, sandwich with filling.

VANILLA COOKIES

These are favourite Christmas biscuits. When you smell them cooking your mouth will water! Here is the recipe.

You will need:
200 g flour
150 g butter
50 g sugar
80 g ground almonds
1 teasp vanilla essence
Icing sugar

Method: Place all ingredients on a board and work together to form a dough. Leave for 20 minutes while you grease a baking tray. Roll out thinly and cut into crescent shapes. Bake for 10 minutes in moderate oven. While still warm, dust with icing sugar.

GINGERBREAD MEN

You will need:
115 g margarine
115 g sugar
3 tablesps golden syrup
1 teasp ground ginger
280 g flour
½ teasp bi-carbonate of soda
White and chocolate icing

Method: Warm fat, sugar and syrup slightly and beat till soft. Add flour, ginger and bi-carb and mix until stiff. Roll out thinly and cut out. Bake in moderate oven for 15–20 minutes — cool on wire tray. Using icing, mark in features and buttons. Or you could trace the design on this page and cut it out in cardboard to use as a pattern for your biscuits. Decorate with pieces of glace cherries.

COCONUT MACAROONS

You will need:
250 g desiccated coconut
250 g sugar
1 teasp cornflour
5 egg whites
Grated rind of one lemon

Method: Wash the lemon, then grate the rind. Whisk egg whites till very stiff. Add sugar and whisk again till stiff. Then fold in coconut, cornflour and rind. Place in spoonfuls on a flour-dusted baking tray and cook in a slow oven for 20 minutes.

KRACKOLATES

You will need:
30 g margarine
1 level tablesp cocoa
Tablesp golden syrup
Tablesp sugar
7 tablesp Cornflakes (or Rice Krispies)

Method: Melt fat and syrup in pan. Do not boil. Add cocoa. Remove from heat and stir in sugar. Using metal spoon, quickly stir cornflakes until coated. Spoon portions into paper cases. Leave to set.

A Walk in a
Christmas Wonderland

On Christmas Eve the snow began to fall, and soon it had made everything white. Three children; Sarah, Rebecca and Peter were feeding the squirrels and birds at the bottom of their garden.

Rebecca offered her cake — a doughnut — to one of the birds to peck at. One squirrel suddenly hopped closer to Sarah and spoke: "As you've been so kind to God's hungry creatures, we hope you will be blessed."

A moment later, Peter, Sarah and Rebecca found themselves being given small presents by a kind old lady. All around them the lamplight glowed golden. It was as if the town had become enchanted.

"Don't worry," said Sarah, the oldest child. "The squirrel told me we would all be blessed. Well, perhaps this is our blessing!"

"That's fine by me!" said Peter. "Because I'd like to ride on that rocking-horse over there."

When Peter and the two girls had each had a turn on the rocking-horse, Sarah stopped to look in a shop window. Rebecca and Peter walked on a few metres and came upon a man who was fixing Christmas trees into wooden bases — so that the trees could stand upright in people's rooms.

Rebecca then saw Santa Claus, with his own tiny Christmas tree and a sack beside him. He gave Rebecca a big red balloon and wished her a Happy Christmas.

Meanwhile, Sarah had been gazing into a shop window. There were toys in the window; a teddybear, a clown, a donkey and a baby deer. "Which toy would you choose, Peter?" she asked.

"I'd choose the donkey," said Peter.

"Oh, I'd pick the teddybear," said Rebecca. "Teddybears are so soft and cuddly!"

"Oh I don't know," sighed Sarah. "I think I would love the clown — because it would make me smile on a rainy day."

The three children walked on and saw a sweet stall ahead of them. On the counter of the stall were some dolls made out of dried plums, wired together and then dressed in clothes of coloured paper.

Suddenly — much to Rebecca's surprise — four of the dolls began to do a little dance on the side of the counter. "I don't believe my eyes!" she cried, "did you see that, Peter?"

"Yes," said Peter. "It's just like a Christmas fairy tale!"

Around the other side of the stall, Sarah had been buying her brother and sister some candy. When she saw the candy, Rebecca soon forgot about the dancing dolls.

As they walked on, the children heard the sound of hooves clip-clopping through the snow. From the pavement they watched as an old Christmas-time carriage pulled by two horses came through the centre of the town. "Perhaps it's carrying some parcels for Santa Claus," suggested Peter.

Rebecca, Sarah and Peter walked on to a quiet part of the town where an old church stood. Its windows were lit up with a welcoming glow, so the children walked towards it. As they walked closer, Peter suddenly saw a golden star falling down from the sky.

The star stopped, and when the children looked again they saw the baby Jesus in a crib. Peter, Sarah and Rebecca knelt beside the crib and left presents there that the old lady had given them. The baby Jesus smiled . . .

Just then (in the Christmas Workshop Bakery) in Heaven — a little angel was taking some dough-nuts to the cupboard.

Suddenly the little angel knew he had to let the cakes fall down to Earth. A little star had told him so.

The angel flew for a moment, and gently tilted the tray of doughnuts until they began falling — falling down towards the town.

On their Christmas Wonderland walk, Peter, Sarah and Rebecca were nearing home, when suddenly Peter cried out with surprise, "Look! It's raining doughnuts!"

"Gosh!" laughed Sarah. "We can take some home with us. It will save our Mother from doing too much Christmas cooking."

"They taste delicious, too!" said Rebecca. "I've never tasted anything like them before. They're ... they're quite heavenly to eat."

When the children went indoors, they found the Christmas Tree set up and presents placed neatly around it. "Did you enjoy your walk in the garden?" asked their mother.

"You wouldn't believe it!" said Peter. "We've seen all kinds of wonderful things like talking squirrels, and stars falling from heaven."

"I would *believe* it," answered their mother. "Because I saw a star fall from heaven too! It landed in the garden, and I've hung it at the top of your Christmas tree!"

When Does Santa Come?

He comes in the night!
He comes in the night!
He softly and silently comes;

While little brown heads
On pillows of white,
Are dreaming of bugles and drums.

He cuts through the snow
Like a ship through the foam,
While the little white snowflakes swirl.

Who tells him? No one knows!
But he finds the bedside
Of each good boy and girl.

He comes in the night!
He comes in the night!
He softly and silently comes.

While little brown heads
On pillows of white,
Are dreaming of bugles and drums.

Christmas Holiday!

Were you up for the dawning
On such a lovely morning?
Did you catch a big smile
From the rising Sun?
Getting up with the birds
Can be such a lot of fun!

Or did you get up very late?
Even after half-past eight?
Or had half-past nine passed
    and gone?
Then you may have had
    breakfast and dinner in one!

While the owl is in bed.
And the cat sleeps in the shed.
The children in this house
Are up and about.
And they'll soon be out to play.
Because they're making the
    most of their Christmas
    holiday!

Ring out wild bells.
Ring out with a chime
For everyone,
This Christmas time.
Sing out you angels.
Sing out with a song
For everyone,
This Christmas Eve morn.

Hear the music play.
At the close of day.
Watch the new stars shine,
Twinkling in time
To that Heavenly rhyme!

Sing Out
With a Song!

Ring out and sing out!
This special night!
Fill the world with song.
Come on! Sing along!
For this is a night
Like no other one.
This is the night
That Jesus was born!

O Christmas Tree

1. O Christmas tree, O Christmas tree, Your branches green delight us. O

Christmas tree, O Christmas tree, Your branches green delight us. They're

green when summer days are bright. They're green when winter snow is white. O

Christmas tree, O Christmas tree, Your branches green delight us.

2. O Christmas tree, O Christmas tree,
You give us so much pleasure.
O Christmas tree, O Christmas tree,
You give us so much pleasure.
How oft at Christmastide the sight
Of green fir tree gives us delight
O Christmas tree, O Christmas tree,
You give us so much pleasure.

3. O Christmas tree, O Christmas tree,
Your dress will teach me something.
O Christmas tree, O Christmas tree,
Your dress will teach me something.
The hope and the constancy
Give power and courage unto me
O Christmas tree, O Christmas tree,
Your dress will teach me something.

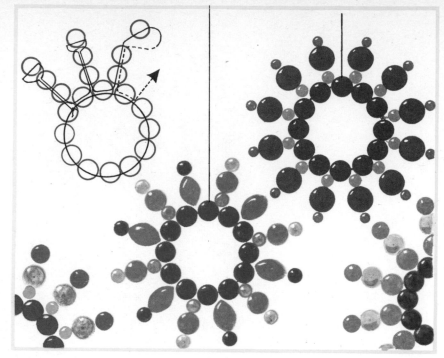

Things
to
Make

A Tree Ornament

You need 12 beads in each of four sizes. On fuse wire thread 12 round beads. Form into a circle leaving one long end of wire. Thread on three more beads (different sizes) then bring wire down through second and first beads, through next one on circle (see diagram), then wire up three more beads, and so on, until you are back where you started. Twist wire between beads to finish off. Tie on a thread or tinsel loop and hang on tree.

A Fir Cone Figure

You will need: Fir cone. Red card. Piece of red ribbon. Tiny piece of fir branch. Small tree toy. A few very short strands of wool. Slice of cork for base. Cotton wool. Portion of nylon tights. Felt tipped pens. Glue. Stick cone upside down on to cork base. Roll cotton wool into ball and wrap in nylon tights material. Mark features with felt pen or cut out pieces of felt for eyes, mouth, cheeks and nose. Stick head to top of cone, and to this stick strands of wool for hair. A semi-circle of card will make his hat.

Trace off these patterns and cut out of red card. Fold the cloak pattern and stick edges. Make cuts down from top point as in Diagram 1. Stick hazelnut on top. Cut two small circles for eyes from black felt or paper and stick in position. Stick on red oval for nose and 2 circles for cheeks. (see picture). Form the hood pattern into a cone as before. Stick on head. Spread glue round edge of hood and bottom half of nut, and on top of hat. Carefully stick on cotton wool. Fold arm pieces in half and stick into place each side of body. Stick on 2 paper or felt buttons.

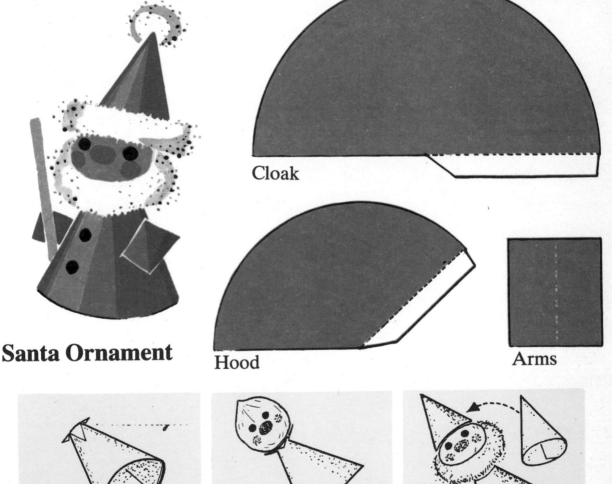

Cloak

Hood

Arms

Santa Ornament

You will need:
Red card
Cotton wool
Black and red sticky paper (or felt and glue)
Hazelnut
Glue

Raisin Men To Eat

These figures are easy to make if you follow the diagrams below. You will need 12 large seedless raisins and a shelled hazelnut for each figure, a piece of marzipan or cork for a base, and strong fuse wire to make skeleton shape. Following diagrams 1, 2, 3 and 4, mould your basic shape.

A THE SWEEP: has a cardboard ladder, a coil of wire with wool tassel for brush and a top hat made from patterns 1, 2 and 3 on page 81. A sugar pig is tucked under one arm and a tiny piece of cloth is used as a neckerchief. Mark a face with coloured pencils.

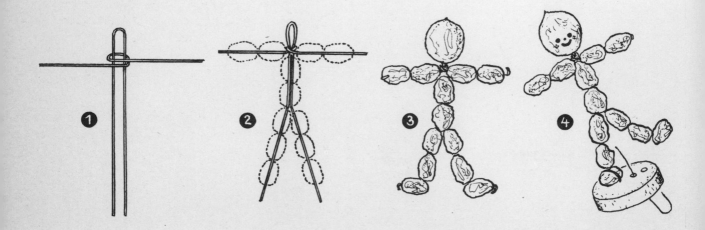

B THE PRESENT BRINGER: is made like the sweep but his body is three dried apricots. Pattern (M) makes his party hat. He has a gift in one hand and a fir branch in the other, a tissue paper scarf and wool strands stuck on for hair.

C A CHRISTMAS REVELLER: He has a top hat like the sweep. His umbrella is made as in diagram (S) on page 81 — with a pipe cleaner centre. A paper collar and tie and cardboard bottle make up his figure.

D THE ZULU: Pattern (K) makes a halo type headdress, with curls of wool for hair. Tiny strings of beads fit neck, wrists and ankles. The skirt is a circle of tissue slashed and tied round her waist. The sack holds coffee.

Coffee

D

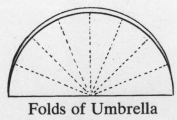

Folds of Umbrella

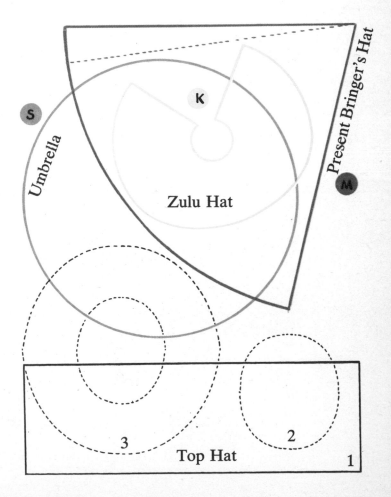

S

Umbrella

K

Zulu Hat

Present Bringer's Hat

M

3

Top Hat

2

1

Writing Christmas Letters

What could be better
  than writing a letter?
So why not drop Santa a line
  this Christmas time?
Or if you've a friend;
  you can always send
  him or her a page or two
  of good wishes and
  Christmas news.
Someone would be glad to
  hear from you
And although a Christmas
  card would do . . .
You could always add a word
  or two,
Like; "Hello! And how are you?"

Sending cards can be such fun —
But then when Christmas time is gone,
You may have some 'thank-you' notes to write
For presents you received on Christmas night.
So try to write a cheery letter
   the happier — the better.
Because if you smile out at the world
Be sure, the world will smile back . . .
Which will be worth much, much more
Than *all* the presents in Santa's sack!

In Christmas-tree Wood

In big woods far away from home
Herds of deer and antelope roam.
Flocks of ravens go flying by
And Christmas trees grow as tall as the sky.

On the forest floor lies a carpet of snow
Which falls through the trees when North winds blow.
And here the squirrels and rabbits play
From sunrise to sunset every day.

Through this wood Anne and Mary were walking
When all of a sudden they heard some elves talking.
"Sshh!" whispered Anne. "Be as quiet as a mouse.
For I think that we've come upon the elves' secret house!"

Just then the door opened and out came an elf.
He said "Hello! Come on in out of the snow!
Come on in and sit by the fire.
Because I expect you're both very tired!"

"We are," said Anne. "And between you and me,
We couldn't half do with a nice cup of tea!"
"Right!" said one elf putting the kettle on the stove.
"Right!" said another elf fetching jam and a loaf.

The elves hung the girls' socks up to dry,
And soon they were all eating hot apple pie.
Anne asked the elves, "Where are all your friends on such
    a cold day?"
Replied the elves, "Look out of the window and you'll see
    them at play . . ."

Turn over the page to see the elves at play.

When the sun did set behind the fir trees
The elves came indoors and all had their teas.
Then out came the tools: it was time for toy-making . . .
At which they were very good
Carving animals and figures out of wood.

They could make a piece of wood come to life
By carving it into a shape with a knife.
Some elves painted the models white,
And then they left them to dry overnight.

The following day they'd paint them once more.
This time all in bright colours galore.
White for a sheep and brown for a horse.
Until all were ready for Santa Claus.

The elves had been so kind to Mary and Anne
That both girls quickly thought of a plan
To help the elves to carry their goods
On the journey to Santa, through the Christmas-tree
    woods.

So Mary and Anne walked all of the way
To Santa's hide-out to borrow a sleigh.
Santa was so pleased with their helpful idea
That he also lent them his fastest reindeer

When Mary and Anne arrived back
They found the elves all ready to pack
Their parcels of toys on to the sleigh.
As soon as this was done, the girls were on their way —
To Santa; with the elves cheering, "Hip, hip, hurray!"

Santa was so pleased with Anne and Mary
That he introduced them both to the Christmas-tree fairy.
The Christmas-tree fairy liked the girls and asked,
"Would you like to help me with my Christmas tasks?"

"You see, I bless everyone's Christmas tree,
And I'll make you both Christmas-tree fairies too,
If you'll be so kind as to help me."

So Mary and Anne got stars for their hair;
And travelled on a magic cloud through the air,
Blessing all Christmas trees in every place
Like Australia, Britain and the United States.

Once their heavenly task had ended
All the Christmas-tree fairies descended.
And Mary and Anne decided to pay
A call on the elves just to say,
"Glad tidings to you on Christmas Day!"

They took a Christmas tree and some gifts
And walked and walked through deep snow-drifts.
They found the elves singing round their own Christmas
    tree
Clapping their hands and dancing with glee.

As soon as the elves saw Mary and Anne
They asked them to join their merry clan.
Some animals came too, swelling the
    happy band;
And soon everyone in Christmas-
    tree Woods had joined hands!

The Little Angel with Silver Hair

The little angel with the silver hair was in trouble. She had been very naughty and now Saint Peter had sent for her. "Come here, naughty one," he said. "You don't seem to understand that everyone here in Heaven has work to do, especially at Christmas time. We all have to make someone on Earth happy." St. Peter frowned. "But you have been lazy and can no longer stay with us. So off you go — you must go down to Earth and make someone happy. Until you do, you can't come back to Heaven."

The very next moment the little angel found herself outside the gates of Heaven. She wondered what to do. So down to Earth she flew and found everything covered in soft white snow. The little angel felt very cold in her thin clothes. The first creature she met was a rabbit who said, "Good afternoon!" The little angel was just about to reply when there was the sound of sleighbells and the patter of hooves. Seconds later, Santa Claus came into view.

When Santa Claus saw the little angel he stopped the sleigh and went over to speak to her. "What are you doing on Earth?" he asked. The angel hung her head with shame and confessed that she had been naughty and lazy in Heaven.

"Lazy, eh?" said Santa. "Then you can come and help me tonight. Hop on to my sleigh!" So saying, Santa tucked the little angel on to the sleigh and off they went. After they had travelled a while, Santa stopped and chose some nice green Christmas trees...

Then he emptied out his sack, which contained Christmas decorations, toys and tinsel. "Would you like to help me to decorate these bare Christmas trees?" asked Santa.

"Oh, yes, I would," replied the little angel with a smile.

"Jolly good," said Santa. "As I'm taller than you, I'll decorate the tops of the trees, and you can decorate their bases."

So Santa and the little angel busied themselves tying the little presents and decorations to the branches of the Christmas trees.

Soon all the toys and tinsel were used up. Santa went off to fetch some bigger presents and promised to collect the little angel on his return. Then the little angel saw that one small tree had no decorations. What could she do? Suddenly she had a marvellous idea! There were gold stars on her dress! She plucked them off and hung them on the branches. What else could she use? Oh! Strands of her beautiful silver hair! These she draped around the tree — and it looked really lovely when she had finished. Even the deer came to admire it!

When Santa Claus returned and saw what the little angel had done, he patted her on the head. "That was a very loving thought," he said. "Now we must take all the trees to the nearest village, and perhaps you can find someone who would like to receive your Christmas tree." So Santa and the little angel hopped aboard the sleigh and Santa drove it through the snow until the twinkling lights of the next village could be seen in the distance.

Santa drove the sleigh into the centre of the village and delivered all his Christmas presents there. The angel helped him in every way she could, until at last the time came for her to deliver her own Christmas tree adorned with her beautiful silver hair and gold stars from her dress.

She carried the tree down the path towards a house where three good children lived. The children were helping their mother to wash the dishes as the angel tip-toed into the house and left the lovely tree, together with some gifts.

The angel left the house and flew around to the living room window, then she gazed inside. She saw the children come out of the kitchen and then sing and dance with delight as they saw the Christmas tree. "Isn't it lovely!" they chorused together. "What kind person could have brought it here for us to share?"

The angel smiled with joy and hurried back to join Santa Claus in the empty sleigh.

"Can I give you a lift anywhere?" asked Santa.

"Yes, please," replied the little angel. "Please take me to the wood where you first found me, then I'll fly back to Heaven from there."

"Right," said Santa, shaking the reins of the sleigh. "And thank you very much for all the help you've given me. I'll make sure Saint Peter hears all about it."

"Thank you and goodbye!" cried the little angel as she flew off into the night.

When the little angel got back to Heaven, Saint Peter was waiting at the door. "Now what have you been doing?" he asked. "Just look at your hair! And where are your gold stars?"

When the little angel told him what had happened to her hair and the gold stars, Saint Peter was very pleased. "Now you can come back into Heaven!" he said.

He was so pleased with the little angel that he gave her some more gold stars and the older angels stitched them on to her robe.

And as for her silver hair ... well, that will grow again!

Making Christmas Decorations

Table Decoration

You will need:
Eight circles of felt in mauve.
Eight round green beads.
Needle and thread.

Thread on the beads and felt as shown in the picture. Tie off the ends of thread, fitting the circle around base of candle. Ask an adult to light the candle for you.

The Snowman

Cover a toilet roll tube (including one end) with white paper as shown. Cut a circle of cardboard 8 cm across. Paint this black and also a 2-cm deep band around the top of the tube. When dry, cut hole in circle of card and pull down over the tube to the edge of black paint. Paint on two eyes and buttons (or cut out in paper and stick on). A red nose and ribbon or paper scarf completes the snowman. If you like you can trim him with a tiny fir branch and toy. He would make a pretty gift for Mummy.

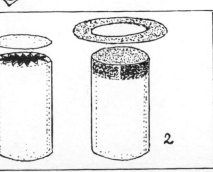

A Coloured Drawing Decoration and a Needle Case

To make the coloured decoration simply trace picture on opposite page on to a piece of white or blue card. Decorate using coloured pencils, cut to shape, then hang on Christmas tree with piece of ribbon. *To make the needle case you will need* 2 pieces of blue felt 11 cm × 11½ cm. 2 or 3 pieces of woollen material. Ribbon for loop 8 cm. Embroidery threads. Needle. Tracing paper. Carbon paper and pencil.

First trace off the design on the next page and using carbon paper transfer the design on to one piece of blue felt. Do the embroidery next, following the stitch diagrams given. Now cut both pieces of felt to the outline shape of

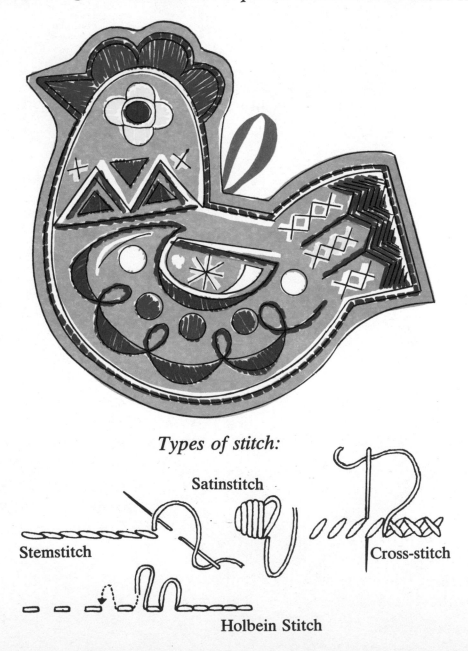

Types of stitch:

Satinstitch

Stemstitch

Cross-stitch

Holbein Stitch

the bird, using the transfer pattern. Cut the woollen pieces slightly smaller; tack them between the two pieces of felt, and at the same time catch in the ends of the ribbon loop for hanging. Now neatly stitch through all thicknesses from top of head to tail of bird. Place one or two needles and a few pins inside to finish off this pretty little gift.

A Scented Wardrobe Sachet

Take two pieces of muslin (or other fine material) 13 × 7 cm. With equal sides together, stitch round, leaving a small opening. Turn to open side. Fill bag with dried lavender (from the chemist). Close the opening, trim bag with lace and add a ribbon loop for hanging. Hasn't it a lovely scent?

Gift Wrapping Ideas

A gift looks better if it is wrapped in lovely paper. Here are some ideas to follow to make your gifts look extra special. If you follow the pictures here you will find a way to wrap most presents.

To make a Pretty Trimming

A rosette on a gift always improves it. Using a pretty ribbon or special wrapping tape, fold it over a piece of card the size you want your rosette. Slip off the card and bind the ribbon in the centre. Tie a short piece of ribbon over the binding thread. Follow the pictures. There is your rosette.

A Hanging Ornament

If you are lucky enough to have a shortbread mould you could make a similar ornament to this. Dust the mould with flour then press it on some rolled out modelling clay. Carefully lift the mould and let the shape dry.

Then paint the embossed parts with poster colours. Glue a ribbon hanger on the back and use as a tree or house ornament.

Oh, Look at the Moon!

Oh look at the moon
She is shining up there
Oh, mother she looks
Like a lamp in the air.

Pretty moon, pretty moon
How you shine on the door
And make it all bright
On my nursery floor.

You shine on my playthings
And show me their place
And I love to look up
At your pretty bright face.

And there is a star
Close by you; and maybe
That small twinkling star
Is *your* little baby.

By Eliza Lee Follen 1787–1860

The Adventures of Nina the Angel

Once upon a time all the angels in Heaven were getting everything ready for Christmas. They were baking biscuits and cakes. They were making puddings and sweets and wrapping gifts for all the children on Earth. They were all very busy except for the youngest angel who was called Nina. She just got in everyone's way. And to make matters worse she ate the biscuits just as soon as they came out of the oven.

Nina had such a sweet tooth that she couldn't resist trying a piece of cake, and even sweets too. Well — you can guess what happened. Nina got a terrible tummy-ache. She was helping some of the other angels when her tummy-ache got worse and worse. In the end she had to sit down on a little fluffy cloud and hold her poor tummy. Great big tears fell from her eyes. Poor Nina!

She was sitting there looking very sorrowful, with a tiny spot of stardust on her nose, when Saint Nicholas found her and took pity on her. "Well, well, well! What's all this?" he asked in a friendly voice. "You come along with me and I'll give you something for your tummy upset." So saying, Saint Nicholas took Nina by the hand and he led her to a little medicine cupboard in the clouds. Here he gave her a spoonful of soothing medicine . . .

Half an hour later, Nina was well enough to go for her music lesson with the other angels. Saint Nicholas was listening to the groups of angels who were singing and playing flutes. Nina joined one of the groups, nearest Saint Nicholas. Soon Saint Nicholas began to hear some funny sounds! He put a hand behind his ear so he could hear better. "Who makes those awful noises?" he asked . . .

Though little Nina was hidden behind the taller angels, Saint Nicholas still found her. "Sorry, Nina," said Saint Nicholas. "I think you'd better not play today. You are making noises as if your flute *had tummy-ache*. Come back another day and practise."

So poor little Nina, who was feeling rather sad, went and sat on the edge of a cloud and listened to the other angels sing. The music was so soothing that Nina fell asleep...

Moments after dropping off to sleep, Nina fell off the edge of the cloud! Before she knew where she was she began falling, falling down to Earth. She was almost down to the ground before she remembered her tiny wings. Fortunately she fluttered them just in time and landed softly in a snowdrift. In the snow covered distance was a little town...

Now Nina was very curious about the Earth, and when she saw a bright light from a window, she couldn't resist peeping in. She saw lovely glowing candles on a Christmas tree and a room filled with toys. Just then a little boy called Peter walked into the room. At first he didn't see Nina at the window. He had just picked up his teddybear when he saw her. "Gosh!" he thought. "I must be dreaming!"

Peter rubbed his eyes and Nina vanished into thin air! But when he looked at the window pane he saw it was speckled with stardust from Nina's nose.

That evening, Peter's mother and father took him to the Christmas Eve service at church. On the way to the church, Peter saw Nina again and pointed to her joyfully. "Look!" he cried. "It's my angel. And here on the snow is some golden stardust!"

"Yes," said his mother patiently. "But now we must hurry along, otherwise we will be late for church."

So with his mother and father, Peter entered the church. He liked to hear the singing in the church, and after prayers the choir began to sing, 'Silent Night, Holy Night'.

Then Peter heard a really beautiful sound. It was a silvery voice which he could hear above all the others. He looked around in wonder, and there upon a pillar near the ceiling he could see the little angel. It was she who was singing so beautifully. Peter smiled at her happily and Nina smiled back.

Late that night Nina travelled back to Heaven. Her little flight to Earth had been very exciting. She had made friends with a boy called Peter, and she had learned what a nice place the Earth could be when everyone sang praises to God. But the greatest thing that Nina discovered was that she had a beautiful singing voice! "Saint Nicholas will be pleased," she smiled. "And tomorrow I'll sing my favourite carol for him ... Silent Night, Holy Night. All is calm, All is bright ..."

The Baby Jesus

The baby comes; comes to us all,
Born at night in Bethlehem's stall.
This blessed night, this holy night:
The star prepared us for the sight.

The shepherds heard the angels sing
Then left their flocks, the message to bring.
The three wise men travelled afar,
Guided by the brilliant star.

We come to the babe in love and awe;
And see what shepherds and wise men saw.
We bring our gifts to our Heavenly King,
And hear angelic hosts now sing,
Glory to God in the highest,
Glory to God our king.

In the Manger

A child is there in the manger
Upon this Christmas day.
We tiptoe softly to see Him
Resting upon the hay.

The children gather round Him
Their treasured gifts to bring.
Seeing their radiant faces,
The Holy angels sing . . .

"Glory to God in the Highest
And peace to men on Earth."
We gather in love together,
To praise our Saviour's birth.

The Good Shepherd

The shepherds watched
Their flocks by day,
Making sure their sheep
Did not go astray.
The shepherds watched
Their flocks by night.
And the stars above
All shone so bright.
But one star shone
With God's own Light.

It showed where the
Baby Jesus lay
On a simple manger
Filled with hay.
And to this day
Our Lord is known
As The Good Shepherd.
As we all have heard.
For we are his sheep
Whose lives he keeps.

Christmastide

Christmas is a gift from Heaven above.
Christmas is hope. Christmas is love.
A time to remember around the tree
A baby born for you — and me.
A time to bask in God's pure light
Through a love that was born one Christmas
 night.
A message that comes to everyone,
Love to all men beneath the sun.

So remember the Christchild and the love he
 brought;
The love that the Kings and Wise men sought.
It can help us remember every day
To live our own lives in God's wise way.

Once Upon a Christmas Time

Lots of snow came falling down
Near a fairy-land town.
It covered everything white,

And the children danced with delight.
Soon they could go out to play
And enjoy the snow in lots of ways.

Like building a snowman three
    metres tall,
Or making a gigantic snowball.
Perhaps going out for a sledge ride,
Or putting on skates and having a
    slide
Across the ice . . .
Wouldn't that be nice?

While the children were playing
  outside,
Someone in red was taking a sleigh
  ride.
Can you guess who the bearded man
  was?
Of course! It was dear old Santa Claus.

This time he was collecting presents
For very poor girls and boys.
And some kind people had given him
   toys
So that all children everywhere
Could share in the Christmas joys.

One warm hearted snowman
Who lived in a winter garden
Liked to watch the children play.

If he only could have spoken,
He would have wanted to say;
To all children, everywhere,
"Oh do have a lovely Christmas day!"

On Christmas Eve, in a garden shed,
(When children are usually in bed)
Some girls and boys gathered to sing

Christmas carols and songs of praise,
Full of heavenly joy and love.
To God, Jesus and the angels,
High in Heaven above.

And up in that starlit heaven
The angels heard the song.
And the song they heard was so
   wonderful —
That they just had to sing along.

"Ding, dong, merrily on high,
In heaven the bells are ringing!
Ding, dong, merrily on high,
In heaven the angels are singing!"

Next day back on earth; evening had
    come.
And the children had all gone home
To play with their toys.

And both girls and boys,
Were happy to say:
"Thank you . . . for a lovely Christmas
    day!"

The Holy Night

"Everyone must go to the city of his birth and register his name there!" ordered the Romans.

It was winter and the nights were cold. Joseph and Mary (who was expecting a child) had travelled a long distance and were very tired. They were on their way to the town of Bethlehem where Joseph had been born. Lots of other people were travelling there too to register their names.

The result was that Bethlehem in the City of David became over-crowded that night, and when the exhausted Joseph and Mary arrived at the Judaean town there was no room at the inn. Joseph told Mary to wait while he searched high and low for a room to sleep in; but every single place was taken, every spare room was occupied.

Then the wife of the innkeeper, hearing of Mary's plight, told them of the stable around the corner. It was the part of the inn where the animals were fed, slept and sheltered. So in that stable, in the still of night, amidst the hay and beside the friendly animals, Mary gave birth to a child called

Jesus. She used the wooden manger of the oxen as his first cradle. In the most humble and yet natural of places; Jesus had finally come to the Earth — the greatest gift of God to mankind.

Nearby, in the dead of night, shepherds were on the hills guarding and caring for their flocks of sheep. One of the shepherds noticed a large bright star, more radiant than any other star in the sky. They were all looking up in wonder at this star, which hung like a jewel in the sky over Bethlehem; when suddenly the Angel of God appeared above them. Then, in a blaze of golden light, the holy angel slowly descended. The angel said: "Fear not. For I bring you good tidings of great joy which shall be for all people. For unto you is born this day, in Bethlehem, a Saviour who is Christ the Lord."

At that moment the sky was filled with a heavenly host, praising God and singing, "Glory to God in the highest, and on Earth let there be peace and goodwill towards all men."

The shepherds could hardly believe their eyes and ears. So they hurried into Bethlehem to find the newly born child, just as the angel had said they would. They found the stable directly under that great and glorious star and inside lay Jesus wrapped in swaddling clothes, sleeping in the manger. The shepherds bowed their heads before the baby.

After this they spread news of the angel's visit, and of the heavenly music which came out of the sky. Then they told of the birth of Jesus — who was to become Christ the Lord.

One day in Jerusalem, the jealous king Herod received news that three wise men from the east were searching for Jesus; and were asking everywhere "Where is he that is born King of the Jews? For we have seen his star in the east and have come to worship him and bear him gifts."

Herod was troubled to learn of this because he thought of himself as king. So he sent for the wise men, and asked them about the star; and they told him they had followed its guiding light for many days.

Herod sent them to Bethlehem and asked "Seek out this child, and when you find him, come and tell me where I might find him also."

So the three wise men followed the star which went before them until it came and stood over the stable where the baby lay, but they did not tell Herod where he was. Then they entered the stable and saw the young child with his mother, and they fell down and worshipped him; and when they had opened their treasures, they presented him with gifts of gold, and frankincense and myrrh. For they knew that before them lay a baby who was the Son of God.

Every year since that day, this story has been told to children all over the world. Since then, too, it has been the custom to give one another gifts. Just as the three wise men gave gifts to the baby Jesus.

Christmas Morning

Christmas morning is a lovely time.
The children's socks all in a line.
Stuffed to the top with exciting things
Like nuts and fruit and a toy on springs.
Crayons and cards, balloons and sweets;
Silver money for children's treats.
Now — off to church some hymns to raise,
To tell of love and joy and praise.

Christmas is about all of these things.
The love and joy the Christchild brings.
He showed us how to love one another;
All our friends and sister and brother.
To spread around that grace he brought
As the child the three wise men sought.
Every year on the 25th December —
It is love we really must remember.

O Joyful Christmastide

1. O thou joyful day, O thou blessed day, Gladsome, peaceful

Christmastide. Earth's hopes awaken, Christ's life hath taken.

Praise him, O praise him, On every side.

2. O thou joyful day.
O thou blessed day.
Gladsome, peaceful Christmastide.
Christ's light is beaming
Our souls redeeming.
Praise him, O praise him
On every side.

3. O thou joyful day,
O thou blessed day.
Gladsome, peaceful Christmastide.
King of glory.
We bow before thee.
Praise him, O praise him
On every side.

166

Silent Night

1. Silent Night, Holy Night! All is calm, all is bright.

'Round yon virgin, mother and child, Holy infant so tender and mild.

Sleep in heavenly peace, Sleep in heavenly peace.

2. Silent Night, Holy Night!
Shepherds quake at the sight.
Glory streams from heaven afar.
Heavenly hosts sing alleluiah.
Christ, the Saviour is born,
Christ, the Saviour is born.

3. Silent Night, Holy Night!
Son of God, love's pure light
Radiance beams from the Holy face,
With the dawn of heavenly grace,
Jesus, Lord at thy birth,
Jesus, Lord at thy birth.

Let us Merrily Dance and Play

1. Let us merrily dance and play:
Santa Claus is on his way
Sing we, sing we, loud and clear,
Christmas Eve will soon be here,
Christmas Eve will soon be here.

2. I'll put out a little dish.
Santa Claus will grant my wish.

3. He will come while I'm asleep,
Dreaming in my slumbers deep.

4. When I wake I'll find a treat.
Lots of lovely things to eat.

5. Let's thank Santa as we should.
Santa Claus is kind and good.

The Story of Muffit
the Little Angel

1st December

This is the beginning of the story of Muffit the little angel. Advent had come, and Advent is the very best time of the year for Muffit. You will soon see why!

Tap, tap, tap! Somebody was knocking at the gates of the Christmas Department of Heaven. St Peter picked up his big bunch of keys and opened the gates with the biggest key of all. He saw a little angel standing outside. The little angel looked around him with awe, and then came shyly in, on tiptoe.

St Peter was about to ask, "And who may you be?" But the little angel didn't seem to be very good at walking on tiptoe. He stumbled, and clutched St Peter's bunch of keys to stop himself falling. St Peter's key-ring opened, and all the keys

fell to the ground. So did the little angel, of course, right on his nose. Poor little thing! He looked miserably up at St Peter. "My — my name's Muffit," he stammered. "I'm from the Stars Department. It was my job to hang the stars up in the sky every evening."

"Indeed!" said St Peter. "And what do you want here in the Christmas Department?"

The little angel looked more miserable than ever. "Well," he said, awkwardly, "you see, I kept on dropping stars. And they fell to Earth as shooting stars. People on Earth like to see shooting stars, but the great

Angel of the Stars wasn't pleased. He called me "Muffit", because if I tried to catch a star I always muffed the catch, and he said I was all thumbs. So I've come here."

St Peter smiled. "And what do you want here?" he repeated.

"I want to help you!" cried the little angel eagerly. "There must be lots of work in the Christmas Department, now that it's nearly Christmas time. I *can* help you, can't I?" And he looked guiltily at the keys lying on the ground.

St Peter looked at them too, but he smiled cheerfully. "We'll find something you can do," he said comfortingly. "There's plenty of work — even for people who are all thumbs! But pick my keys up first, will you? When you're my age, bending's not as easy as it used to be. And once you've collected them all, put them down on that cupboard. I'm in rather a hurry — I must be going."

And with these words St Peter turned and went away.

There sat Muffit, surrounded by St Peter's keys. He had to pick them all up — but then he'd be allowed to stay here! Here, in the Christmas Department of Heaven! That meant he could be useful, even if he was all thumbs. He felt so proud he forgot everything else — including the keys he was supposed to pick up. Muffit gazed happily into space, lost in his daydreams.

The Letter Angel

It was late one evening not long before Christmas. The little village was covered with snow. All was quiet and peaceful, and nothing moved. This was the Letter Angel's time to go round the houses.

The Letter Angel was still quite small, and this was her first journey to Earth. She flew from window to window, collecting the letters children had written saying what they wanted for Christmas. It was hard work! She was perspiring, in spite of the cold.

Her bag was soon full of letters
addressed to Santa Claus.

There were so many things the children wanted! Just a few more houses, and then her work was done. She set off on the long way home. Once she reached the Christmas Department of Heaven, she sat down with the other angels and began sorting through the letters. "What a wonderful time Earth children have!" she sighed. "They get such lovely presents for Christmas! But nobody thinks of all the little angels — yet we're the ones who are kept so busy granting their wishes!"

The other little angels were happily
working away.

The little angels packed up teddy bears and dolls and even a doll's pram in brightly coloured boxes. Then they did the boxes up in gift wrapping paper, and last of all they tied pretty ribbons round them. All the other Christmas Letter Angels were enjoying the work, but our own little angel was feeling sadder and sadder. Big tears welled up in her eyes and trickled down her cheeks. Now and then she wiped a tear away, but more of them kept on coming.

The other angels couldn't make it out! They had been doing this work for years and years, and it had always made them very happy.

There were only a few more presents left to wrap, and then the little angels could take all the parcels down to Earth.

*This was the moment all the little angels
looked forward to most every year.*

But our own little angel just couldn't cheer up.

The Christmas Angel, who was about to fly down to Earth, saw the little angel weeping. Nobody could comfort her. So the Christmas Angel simply took her hand, and they flew down to Earth together. She was to be allowed to help with the most important work! They decorated a Christmas tree.

The little angel hung sweets and biscuits and coloured glass balls on the tree. In came the Christmas Angel through the open window, carrying a teddy bear and a doll. There was already a toy train standing at the foot of the tree. Those were the presents for the children who lived in the house.

As she worked, the little angel forgot her sadness. She clapped her hands happily, but the other angel whispered, "Ssh!" They didn't want the children to hear them. Then they went on to the next house.

At last there was a decorated Christmas tree in every house, and all the presents were in their places. They had all done their work. The little angel heaved a sigh of relief.

Now it was time to go back to the Christmas Department of Heaven. They were almost out of the village when the little angel saw a brightly lit window. Feeling curious, she went over to the house.

The first thing she heard was the sound
of children's happy voices.

She went a little closer to the window and peered in. There was so much to look at on the other side of the glass! How happy they all were around the Christmas tree! Children were dancing merrily about. You could see how pleased they were with all their presents — and that made the little angel happy too. She didn't mind not having a present of her own any more. The children's happiness was infectious! She flew on from house to house, looking in at the windows.

And everywhere she went, she saw happy faces.

The little angel's sadness was all gone, for the best Christmas present the angels can have is the sight of happy, cheerful children around a Christmas tree.

The Christmas Letter Angel never tired of looking in at them. Several times, she started off back to Heaven, but again and again she flew down to look in one more window. At last, however, she did set off for home, singing happily.

So the little Christmas Letter Angel had a very happy Christmas after all.

The Story of Muffit the Little Angel

2nd December

Muffit felt very important all of a sudden! He was going to be allowed to help in the Christmas Department! He raised his head proudly — and knocked it against the edge of a table. That brought him back from his dreams. He was supposed to be picking up St Peter's keys, and he'd better get a move on! Oh, what a nuisance — one key had fallen right underneath the big cupboard. Muffit had to crawl under it himself, and he was just reaching for the key, when something bumped into his legs. Muffit shot out from under the cupboard. A book fell on his head — and more books were tumbling to the ground all around him.

Muffit saw another little angel looking at him in surprise. "Oh dear — I'm sorry, I didn't see your legs!" said the angel. "Where were you?"

"Under the cupboard!" said Muffit, crossly. "I was trying to get at that key, and you gave me such a fright I've left it there!"

"Another scatterbrain!" laughed the other angel. "I'm scatterbrained myself — that's why they call me Scatty!"

"And my name's Muffit," said Muffit, "but I'm not scatterbrained. It's just that I'm all thumbs!"

The Story of Muffit the Little Angel

3rd December

So there stood the two little angels, just inside the gates of Heaven. Muffit helped Scatty to pick his books up. They were chattering happily away as they worked.

Suddenly a door opened, and a cross voice shouted, "What's all this noise about? We need peace and quiet in here — we're busy writing the stories for children's picture books. But with all this racket—"

However, the voice didn't finish what it was saying, because suddenly the air was full of sheets of paper blowing about.

How funny, thought Muffit. Everything goes flying through the air here in the Christmas Department: first keys, then books, now sheets of paper!

A gust of wind had blown through an open window in the story-writing room. "And kindly pick those papers up!" the voice told Muffit and Scatty, and then the door was closed again.

Chuckling, the two little angels picked them all up. Muffit handed them in through the doorway.

Then there was another crash. Scatty put both hands to his forehead. "Oh, how silly!" he said. "Now I've gone and forgotten where I was supposed to take those books!"

"That's no reason to drop them again!" said Muffit.

"Did I really?" said Scatty, sounding very scatterbrained indeed.

Christmas Cookery

Do you like biscuits? Here's a recipe for some Christmas biscuits you can make at home. Maybe Mother will help you. For instance, you could ask her to turn the oven on — it needs to be heated before the biscuits go in. Tell her to set it at a temperature of 150°C/300°F/gas mark 2.

Spice Cookies
You will need:
125g/4oz sugar
125g/4oz ground almonds or hazelnuts
½ a lemon
1 pinch ground cinnamon
1 pinch ground cloves
1 egg white

Place all the ingredients on a big wooden board. Wash the lemon half, grate its peel finely over the other ingredients. Mix everything well together with your hands to make a dough. Roll it out quite thickly. Use small cutters to cut out little shapes. Butter a baking sheet and put the biscuits on it. Bake them in the oven for 30 minutes. When they are cooked, take them straight off the baking sheet — use a spatula, not your fingers! — and let them cool on a cake rack.

And then they are ready to eat!

The Story of Muffit the Little Angel

4th December

Muffit and Scatty, the two little Christmas angels, stood looking at Scatty's books. They didn't know what to do. Where were the books supposed to go?

"Can I help you?" asked a familiar voice. It was St Peter. He looked at the books. "Why, those belong to Santa Claus!" he cried. "You must take them to him straight away. He needs them — it's urgent!"

On their way to Santa Claus, Muffit asked, "What's inside those books?"

"They say whether children have been good or bad," Scatty told him, "and the good children get presents at Christmas."

"What about the bad children?" asked Muffit.

"I don't know that there *are* any really bad children," said Scatty.

"That reminds me of something," said Muffit. "There were two little sisters who were always quarrelling. You could hear them right up here in Heaven! When it was time to tidy up their toys, they both used to say, 'That's not mine, *you* must tidy it up!' But when they were going to play, they both said, 'That's mine, *you* can't play with it!' However, just before Christmas their house suddenly went very quiet. They'd stopped quarrelling. Isn't it funny how that kind of thing always happens around Christmas time?"

Scatty thought for a few moments. "Do you think children are good only so that they'll get toys?" he asked. "I wonder!"

A Little Child There is Y-Born

1. A little child there is y-born,
Eia, eia, susanni, susanni, susanni,
And he sprang out of Jesse's thorn,
Alleluya, alleluya,
To save all us that were forlorn.

2. Now Jesus is the childes name,
And Mary mild she is his dame;
And so our sorrow is turned to game.

3. It fell upon the high midnight,
The stars they shone both fair and bright.
The angels sang with all their might.

4. Three kings there came with their presents
Of myrrh and gold and frankincense,
As clerkes sing in their sequence.

5. Now sit we down upon our knee
And pray we to the Trinity
Our help, our succour for to be.

The Story of Muffit the Little Angel

5th December

Muffit and Scatty, the two little angels, arrived at Santa's door. They were about to open it when they had to jump aside in a hurry, for the door flew open — and out came a bush! But it was no ordinary bush, dear me, no! It had no leaves on it, and it was covered with sweets and biscuits instead. Muffit saw that it had a pair of legs too.

"Oops-a-daisy — watch out there!" said whoever was behind the bush.
Crash! The door slammed.

"That must have been Noisy — it's the way he always shuts doors," the bush explained. "Who are you? My name's Oops-a-daisy."

All that could be seen of Noisy was the big sack he was carrying. Several other little angels followed him out of the door. They were carrying sacks full of the presents Santa was sending children, and Oops-a-daisy was holding his bundle of twigs covered with good things to eat.

"My books! At last!" said a deep voice. And Muffit felt very excited, because there he was, face to face with Santa himself.

The Christmas Flower

This Christmas story comes from the land of the gnomes. Grouchy George was a garden gnome — and a gardener gnome, too! He had some magic powder he could sprinkle over plants to make the most beautiful flowers bloom.

But the trouble with Grouchy George was that he was so unfriendly!

It all started a few weeks before Christmas. The whole of Gnomeland was already covered with snow. Grouchy George came running out of his little house, the way he did every morning. And it just so happened that the squirrels were always leaping around his garden at that time of the morning, looking for pine cones. Grouchy George always chased them away. He didn't want any squirrels in his garden. He didn't want any cats there either, or any birds — and he certainly didn't want any other gnomes. You'd have thought Grouchy George actually liked losing his temper!

But today he forgot to shoo the squirrels off. He stood and stared at the snow before him in surprise. There was a plant growing there! It had buds on it, too, as if it were going to flower in spite of the cold weather. And yet he hadn't seen a trace of that plant yesterday!

Grouchy George scratched his head thoughtfully. He had no idea what the plant was called. He really was a very good gardener, but he had never seen a plant like this before.

"I know!" he thought, and he fetched his magic powder. "If I sprinkle a little powder over the plant, it will flower," he told himself, "and then I'll know what it is!"

So he sprinkled a whole handful of his powder over the plant, and then another and another — but the buds stayed closed. Such a thing had never happened before!

"Go on, will you — flower!" he told the plant crossly. He emptied the whole bag of magic powder over it. He fetched his watering can and watered it. But the mysterious plant just stayed the way it was.

Now what? Grouchy George couldn't think of anything else to do. He would simply have to wait. The buds would probably open to-morrow — or the day after tomorrow, at the latest!

Next morning he stood in front of that plant for hours on end. Nothing happened. He waited in vain next day, too. The birds and the squirrels were very surprised. They could play about around him undisturbed. He didn't even notice them.

Time passed by. Christmas was coming in Gnomeland. The postman had lots of parcels to deliver, and all the gnomes tried to be specially nice to each other.

All the gnomes? Well, all but one. Perhaps it was because of that stupid flower, but Grouchy George's temper had been even worse than usual for some days. All the same, some of the other gnomes did come to knock on his door now and then. "Would you like to come out into the forest with us and feed the animals?" they asked. Or, "Have you got anything to give poor old Widow Woodspurge? She has no one to think of her at Christmas!"

But Grouchy George just went red in the face with anger. "What do I care about the animals?" he said crossly. "Why should I bother with old Widow Woodspurge? Nobody gives *me* anything for Christmas either! And nobody can get my plant to flower!" Then he would slam the door and shut the other gnomes out, he was so furious! But none of this did him any good. The buds on his plant just would not open. Was it trying to annoy the impatient garden gnome on purpose?

So in the end Grouchy George was angry with everyone and everything. He was angry with the flower because it wouldn't bloom, and angry with the gnomes because they got on his nerves.

He felt as if he could think of nothing else in the world until that plant flowered, and he was cross with the other gnomes because they didn't understand. What do *you* think? Ought Grouchy George to have gone to feed the animals with them?

Grouchy George went and looked at his flower every day. There was no point in it, since he had no way of making it bloom, but he didn't want to do anything else either. He could see the other gnomes out of the corner of his eye. How busy they all seemed! Couldn't they think of anything better to do than running about from house to house the whole time, George wondered angrily. Poor George! He honestly thought that *he* was doing something better!

Soon the other gnomes stopped bothering about him. He would only have sent them away again, anyway. And nobody wanted to have that cross garden gnome spoiling the fun of looking forward to Christmas. So after a while none of them came knocking at Grouchy George's door at all. He was by himself all day, every day, without so much as a visitor he could shout at.

This was something new for Grouchy George. When he opened his mouth it was only to say something cross — but he didn't like not having anyone at all to talk to, not a bit! First he felt angry with the other gnomes. "Fancy ignoring me like that!" he muttered. But now he had plenty of time to think. And it struck him that he really *had* been rather bad-tempered recently. In the end he told himself, sighing, "I suppose it's no wonder they don't like me. I don't like myself much these days!"

Oh dear — Grouchy George was in a bad way. He cast one last, despairing glance at that plant and went indoors. Now he knew how Widow Woodspurge would feel if the gnomes forgot her at Christmas. He felt just the same!

Christmas Eve came. The gnomes hurried from house to house, wishing each other the compliments of the season. But all was quiet in Grouchy George's house. Sometimes he heard the faint sound of a voice calling, "Happy Christmas!" But it wasn't meant for him.

It's no fun to be alone. Especially when you can see how happy all the others are together!

Grouchy George looked out of the window. He felt more miserable than he had ever been in his life. Even that plant didn't want anything to do with him!

"Poor George!" said his neighbours. "Why is he so cross with us? We'd have liked to ask him round — but he wouldn't have come!"

Well, by now he might have come! For all of a sudden, George wished he had some friends. Most of all he wished he wasn't alone now, on Christmas Eve. But he was too proud to go and ask if he could come in and spend Christmas with the others.

Slowly the noise in the gnome village died down. Doors were closed, and darkness fell. Grouchy George saw bright lights coming on in all the windows. Now and then he heard the strains of a Christmas carol.

And then he thought of something. He turned and ran off to his store-room, and he could be heard in there for quite a while, rummaging around. At last he reappeared, carrying a bottle of blackberry wine. He locked his front door and ran off like the wind. Where could he be going? Several gnomes in the village looked out of their windows and said, "Grouchy George is behaving very oddly these days! There he goes at the run!" Still, why bother about such a bad-tempered gnome today? It was Christmas, and the others wanted to be happy.

And so did George! That was why he was running through the snow-covered forest with his bottle of blackberry wine, getting it all shaken up. In his haste he had even forgotten his jacket. But running warmed him — and so did a feeling inside him that he had not felt for quite a long time.

The woodland animals watched in surprise as he passed by. What was he up to, disturbing the peace of their quiet forest?

Soon Grouchy George could see a faint light among the trees. He was running towards it. It came from the little house where Coachman Jack lived.

Coachman Jack had once been a very important person in Gnomeland. Years ago, he used to drive the gnome mail-coach, and the gnomes travelled all over the country in it. But then the gnome railway was built, and suddenly there were no more passengers for the coach. None of the gnomes wanted to ride in it now — they wanted to travel by train. And all of a sudden Jack felt he was no use for anything. He didn't want the others to see how miserable he was, so he went away to live in a little house in the forest, and soon the rest of the gnomes forgot all about him.

Today, however, Grouchy George had suddenly remembered him. He was going to ask if he could spend Christmas with Coachman Jack. Because Jack didn't know how nasty he had been to the other gnomes, and he hadn't seen the mysterious plant either. In fact, it was a long time since he had known about anything that went on in the gnome village.

George stood at the door, knocking. "What will Jack say when he sees me?" he asked himself. Suddenly, he was worried. Suppose Jack didn't want anything to do with any gnomes? Suppose he sent him straight off? Suppose he wasn't even at home?

He almost turned to go back home himself — but then the door was opened, and it was too late. Coachman Jack was looking surprised. "Why, George!" he cried in astonishment. "Have you lost your way?"

Rather shyly, Grouchy George held out the bottle of blackberry wine. "Er . . . happy Christmas!" he stammered. "I . . . er . . . came to wish you the compliments of the season, Jack!" And he tried to keep his face hidden behind the bottle, so that Coachman Jack wouldn't see how red it had gone.

"I thought . . . I was wondering . . . well, I wondered if you'd like company at Christmas?" There — now he'd said it! "But if you'd rather be on your own, just say so, and I'll be off!" George added, rather uncertainly.

Coachman Jack had been staring at him, open-mouthed, but now, slowly, he found his tongue again. "No, no — don't go away! Of course I'd like company — I'd like it very much indeed! Only I wasn't expecting it. I don't know what to say!"

Now George saw that Jack's face was as red as his own, and he felt better. "And I brought you this bottle of blackberry wine!" he said.

Jack realized that they were still standing in the doorway. "What are we doing out here in the cold?" he said happily. "Come on in! I think I even have some wine-glasses somewhere, if I look for them!"

Sure enough, Jack found two handsome wine-glasses hidden away in a very dusty corner. He put them on the table, and George poured out the blackberry wine.

After the first sip, Jack said, "I don't believe I ever tasted such good blackberry wine before!"

"I think everything tastes better if you're feeling happy," said George.

"How long is it since we last saw each other?" Jack asked suddenly.

"Let's see," said George, thoughtfully. "Wasn't it two years ago, when we met by chance in the forest?"

"Oh yes — I remember now!"

There's a lot to say when you haven't seen each other for so long. George and Jack sat in the warm and talked and talked, and as they talked they drank George's good blackberry wine.

"Things were better when the mail-coach still ran," said George. "You should just hear the things the gnomes say when the train's late again!"

Jack laughed. "I used to hate the railway," he said. "But believe it or not, I'd rather like to go in a train myself now. Perhaps they'd let me be coachman on the train!"

"Trains don't have coachmen, they have engine drivers," George told him. "But we could go for a train ride together, if you like."

Jack thought that was a good idea. "Come on!" he cried, jumping up from his chair.

"You mean you'd come back to the village with me?" said George. He could hardly believe his ears.

"Of course!" said Coachman Jack. "You've no idea how much I'd like to see everything there!"

So they both set off to walk home to George's house. It was the nicest walk George had ever had.

The woodland animals watched them pass by in surprise. And how surprised the other gnomes were when they got back to the village!

"Grouchy George and Coachman Jack!" said the gnomes, in amazement. "What can have brought those two together?"

And how happy the gardener gnome was now! George wasn't grouchy any more! He was singing Christmas carols and beaming all over his face.

But the other gnomes felt rather guilty. They had Coachman Jack on their consciences. They had forgotten all about him, even at Christmas, and yet they had tried to remember all lonely gnomes.

"We'll have our train ride, but not until tomorrow," said George. "Today I'm inviting everyone to my house, for a Christmas party. And I'll try not to lose my temper any more!"

What fun! Of course all the gnomes were happy to come to the party, because they really liked George — they just didn't like it when he was so cross! But that was all over now.

However, the biggest surprise of all was waiting for George outside his house. His plant was in bloom! Three beautiful flowers had opened on it in the middle of the snow.

George stopped and stared at it. "Go on into the house, everyone!" he said. "I'll be with you in a minute." And he stood and looked at the plant with awe.

This was the first day he had wanted to give someone else pleasure — and today his plant had flowered! Did those two things have anything to do with each other! I think they did! The flowers didn't want the cross gnome to see them, so they stayed shut when Grouchy George looked at them. But now he wasn't grouchy any more — he was kind, and smiling. The flowers didn't mind looking at *that* sort of gnome. He didn't even need his magic powder to make them open.

Since that time, the plant outside his door has flowered every year, and the buds have never refused to open for him. George has learnt his lesson.

Christmas roses flower in other parts of the world too — and always at Christmas time. And there will always be people who have no one to think of them at Christmas time too. Perhaps Christmas roses are to remind us of those lonely people.

The Story of Muffit the Little Angel

6th December

I expect you would like to know how Muffit and Scatty, the two little angels, had been getting on. Well, they had their hands full just now, for they had to help Santa Claus on his visit to Earth.

"Come along," said Santa, "we must go down to Earth, where the children are expecting me!" And he told the angels to hurry.

Muffit and Scatty joined the other little angels. They were sure no one would mind — and they did want to go down to Earth too, and help Santa choose who to give his presents to.

They began climbing down the ladder from Heaven. Earth slowly came closer. But Santa was very slow, and stout, and the angels soon felt bored. They began to play Catch, chasing each other up and down the ladder. But Muffit wasn't taking care, and he missed a rung and fell off . . . it's a good thing angels can fly!

Santa was cross. "That's quite enough playing about!" he growled. "I very nearly fell off myself. Just think what the children would say if Santa came down to Earth with a broken leg!"

Santa warned Noisy not to slam doors when he was going round the houses, and said he did not want to hear Oops-a-daisy's favourite word either. He told Scatty to hold the books properly, and not upside down! And Muffit was to try not to be all thumbs when he did anything.

The children were waiting anxiously for Santa and his helpers. And soon all those children would be very, very happy — so happy that most of them wouldn't even notice Santa and the angels leaving.

Late that night they all met back in the Christmas Department of Heaven, tired but very happy. Muffit and Scatty couldn't stop talking. They had had such a lovely time today, and they simply had to go over it all again and again.

Muffit was very pleased. Yes, he *was* all thumbs, there was no denying it — but today he had made himself really useful. He had helped Santa, and he had looked into many, many shining pairs of children's eyes. Muffit was the happiest angel in Heaven.

Ring, Sweet Bell

1. Ring, sweet bell, tingalingaling, ring, sweet bell, ring
Children, it is snowing, icy winds are blowing.
In the cold midwinter, children, let me enter.
Ring, sweet bell, tingalingaling, ring, sweet bell, ring.

2. . . . Hear my bell a-ringing.
Presents I am bringing.
Games and books and fine toys,
for good girls and good boys.
Ring, sweet bell . . .

The Story of Muffit the Little Angel

7th December

It was late at night in the Christmas Department of Heaven, but Muffit and Scatty didn't feel a bit sleepy.

Perhaps the same thing has happened to you: if you've had a very exciting day you can't get to sleep however tired you are! That was just how Muffit and Scatty felt. They were sitting up in bed, talking.

"That little boy called Peter was the one I liked best," said Muffit. "He will be so pleased with his toy horse!"

"No wonder!" Scatty told his friend. "He wanted that horse for Christmas last year. And a lot of parcels arrived before Christmas Day, and Peter did want to know what was in them! So one day, when his mother was out, he made a little hole in the wrapping paper of one parcel with his finger and saw the toy horse inside. But of course his mother noticed the hole, and she sent the horse straight back to the Christmas Department here. Poor Peter was very sad when Christmas came and he didn't get the little horse after all. But he's tried not to be so nosy ever since, so Santa said he could have a horse this year. Would you like a biscuit, Muffit?"

"I've got some biscuits of my own, thank you," said Muffit.

"Ouch!" squealed Scatty suddenly. "I'm sitting on one of mine! It must be a star-shaped biscuit — it has such sharp points! Ouch!"

The Story of Muffit the Little Angel

8th December

Muffit still hadn't found out what someone who was all thumbs would be really good at, so they told him he could look around the Christmas Department for a while. He decided to start in the kitchen, where good things were being baked for Christmas. Such tempting smells floated out through the doorway!

It was hot in the kitchen. All the little angels were scurrying about, red in the face, mixing dough, cutting out biscuits, taking baking sheets out of the oven. Muffit was eager to join in. But the first thing he did was to drop an egg on the floor.

Then somebody shouted, "I need another sack of flour!" Muffit ran to fetch it — but on his way back he trod on the broken egg, slipped and fell, and the sack burst. A cloud of white flour spread through the whole room. All the little angels had to sneeze, and Muffit sneezed loudest of anyone, because he had got the most flour up his nose.

When he had finished sneezing, he had to laugh. "Ha, ha, ha — just look at you!" he chuckled. And he pointed at the other little angels. "You're all as white as snow!"

But he soon stopped laughing when they told him he must sweep up all the flour!

O Christmas Tree

1. O Christmas tree, O Christmas tree!
Thou tree most fair and lovely!
The sight of thee at Christmas-tide
Spreads hope and gladness far and wide.
O Christmas tree, O Christmas tree!
Thou tree most fair and lovely!

2. O Christmas tree, O Christmas tree!
Thou hast a wondrous message.
Thou dost proclaim the Saviour's birth,
Goodwill to men and peace on earth.
O Christmas tree, O Christmas tree!
Thou has a wondrous message.

The Story of Muffit the Little Angel

9th December

Muffit the little Christmas angel had to sweep out the kitchen of the Christmas Department of Heaven. When he had finished, he decided to try some cooking again. He'd do better this time! He filled some little moulds with a chocolate-flavoured mixture, to make chocolate biscuits. But the moulds were rather small for somebody who was all thumbs, and the chocolate kept spilling over the sides. Muffit just wiped it off with his fingers, and then wiped his fingers clean on his apron. He was feeling very pleased with himself — until a voice called out, "Just look! Here's a little chocolate angel!"

Sure enough, he was covered with chocolate! Muffit went to find a clean apron, feeling rather ashamed. But this time he really *would* do better! When chocolate spilled over the sides he simply licked it off, and his apron stayed nice and white.

Crash! The door slammed. Muffit was so startled that he dropped his bowl of chocolate, and the chocolate splashed all over him. But strange to say, he hardly noticed, for suddenly he realized he wasn't feeling at all well. Licking off all that chocolate didn't agree with him.

Muffit sat down — right on a tray full of chocolate biscuits!

Of course it was Noisy who had slammed the door so loud. Noisy saw what the matter was at once. He took Muffit's hand.

"You should be in bed!" he said. "Come along — I'll help you." And he led poor
Muffit, who was looking very white in the face, out of the kitchen. As they went,
you could have heard a little click-click-clicking sound — it was made by the
chocolate biscuits sticking to Muffit, which were now dropping off him and landing
on the floor.

Christmas Decorations

Would you like to make this funny Father Christmas to hang on the Christmas tree?

You will need:

2 triangles of red felt, with each side 8.5cm/3¼ inches long

1 small red paper circle, 2 small black paper circles (cut them out with a paper puncher!)

1 sheet of white paper

black paper for the moustache

glue   string

Stick the two triangles of felt together. Trace Section 2 in the diagram on white paper and cut the shape out. Cut into the lower semicircle to make the fringed beard. Stick the beard and face in the middle of the triangle. Stick on the paper circles for eyes and nose. Trace the moustache on black paper, cut it out and stick it on the face. Thread the string through the top of Father Christmas's hat, and then you can hang him on the Christmas tree.

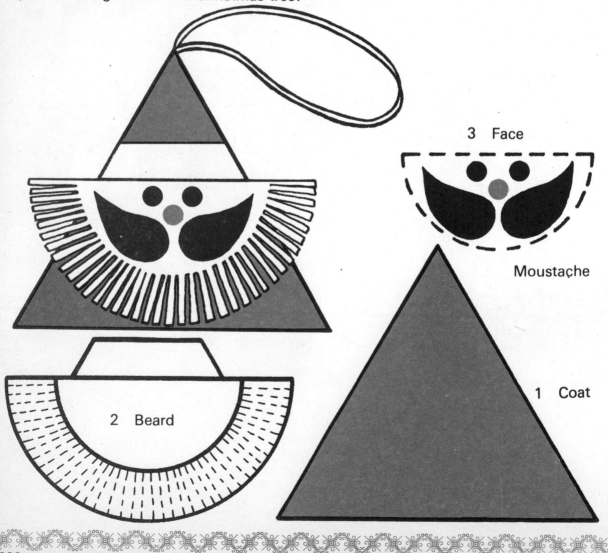

3   Face

Moustache

2   Beard

1   Coat

Christmas in the Forest

It was Christmas Eve. All the rooftops were thickly covered with snow, and glittered in the setting sun. Suddenly the sound of sleigh bells was heard in the forest near by. Could it be Santa Claus? Yes, of course it was Santa Claus on his way — and high time, too! Lights were beginning to go on in the houses, and the children were already waiting, looking hopeful and excited. But look at the funny trail Santa Claus was leaving behind him,

Nuts and apples and sugar biscuits had fallen to the ground as the sleigh went along. They came through a hole in Santa Claus's sack. The little angels had forgotten to mend it. Along came a little deer and sniffed at one of the biscuits. Soon the fox and the squirrel joined him. Hoppy the hare and Squeaker the mouse had seen what was happening,

and they came along too.

Before long, all the good things had been eaten up, and there was nothing left but a pair of slippers lying in the snow. The animals sniffed them all over, but the slippers were no good to any of them.

"Perhaps the Goblin will know what to do with them," said Hoppy the hare. So the animals all set off for the house under the tree root at the edge of the forest, where the Goblin lived.

The Goblin was excited because it was Christmas Eve, too. "Hullo, Goblin!"

on the deep snow of the forest land!

"There's a pair of slippers in the forest," they told him. "We wondered if they'd fit you!"

Since the snow was so deep, the little deer let the Goblin ride on his back.

They soon found the slippers. The Goblin put them on — but I'm afraid they were far too big for him!

Now what? They couldn't just leave such a good pair of slippers lying in the snow. "I know!" said the Goblin. "There's an old woman who lives on the edge of the forest. If we took her this pair of slippers,

I'm sure she'd be glad of them!"

"What a good idea!" said the animals. And they all set off together. The fox carried one slipper, and the squirrel carried the other. It wasn't easy walking through the deep snow with the slippers, but at last they reached the old woman's cottage. They saw a light in one of the windows. So they put the slippers down on the doorstep, and then hid.

The old woman had heard some strange rustling, pattering sounds outside, and she opened her door to see what was going on.

The animals were all watching!

The old woman saw a pair of slippers on her doorstep. Such beautiful slippers, too! Fancy that! Uncertainly, she picked them up and stroked the soft velvet. She had never had such a lovely pair of slippers in her life.

The animals and the Goblin held their breath as they watched from their hiding places.

The old woman went back into her cottage with the new slippers, shaking her head. She couldn't make it out.

"That was a good idea of yours, Goblin!"

said the animals, when she had gone.

Hoppy the hare and the fox looked curiously through the window. How pleased they were to see that the new slippers fitted the old woman as if they had been made for her!

On their way home the animals met Santa Claus. He was coming back from leaving his presents. They had all been given away, and his sack was quite empty.

"Never mind!" said Hoppy the hare. "We found a lot of nice things lying in the snow a little while ago.

You did mean them for us, didn't you?"

Santa Claus smiled. He had noticed the hole in his sack. Well, at least he knew where the things had gone now!

"And we gave the slippers to the old woman who lives in the cottage at the edge of the forest," the Goblin said. Santa Claus was pleased to hear that, because he had been going to take her the slippers anyway! "If you're so good at giving presents," he said wearily, "then you can all help me next year. And then, at least,

I won't be as tired as I am today!"

"Of course we'll help you!" said the animals happily. "Goodbye, Santa, until next year!"

And they all ran merrily off to the Goblin's house. But what was this? They could hardly believe their eyes! There was a beautifully decorated Christmas tree standing outside the little house under the tree root, with a manger for the animals and a bird table beside it.

"Oh, how lovely!" cried the Goblin. "Now we can all have a Christmas party together!"

The animals were delighted too.

They all stood around the Christmas tree with its bright candles, and felt happier than they had ever been in all their lives.

Living in the forest is nice, thought the Goblin. He looked lovingly at his friends. They were quiet and full of awe, and their eyes shone. But Christmas in the forest is best of all, thought the Goblin.

"Where's the little deer?" Hoppy the hare asked.

"Ssh!" said Squeaker the mouse. "He's gone to sleep."

And of course he was having sweet dreams.

The Story of Muffit the Little Angel

10th December

Our friend Muffit the little angel was feeling better. He had made himself ill, eating chocolate in the kitchen of the Christmas Department of Heaven — do you remember? Now he felt ashamed of himself. All the other angels had laughed, and he was afraid to face them again. If they laugh at me any more I'll run away, he thought.

But as he reached the kitchen he heard his friend Noisy inside, telling the other little angels a story.

"Once upon a time there was a giant called Ernest. His name was Ernest because he was very earnest and serious and never laughed. And there was a dwarf called Merry, because he was always merry and laughing. The two of them did not get on with each other.

One day Ernest the giant saw Merry the dwarf pulling a heavy cart uphill and whistling cheerfully to himself. But when at last he reached the top of the slope, he carelessly let go of the cart too soon, and it rushed away downhill again. That made the dwarf angry. And he was even angrier when he saw Ernest, for the giant was watching him — and laughing! Merry felt very, very cross indeed. You see, Merry had one big failing: he was good at laughing at other people, but he couldn't laugh at himself."

Muffit felt better. He was sure Noisy had told that story specially to make things easier for him!

The Christmas Candles all are Burning

1. The Christmas candles all are burning,
the Christmas tree is green and bright,
as if, with every year returning,
it showed that Hope is here tonight.

2. Two holy angels softly enter,
unseen by any human eye,
pray by the tree in the room's centre,
and leave a blessing from on high.

The Story of Muffit the Little Angel

11th December

When Muffit joined the other little angels again, not one of them laughed at him. They had learnt their lesson from the story Noisy told them.

Then Oops-a-daisy came rushing in. "Oops-a-daisy!" he called. "I say, I've been reading some of the letters children write saying what they'd like for Christmas! The things some children want! One little boy says he wants the last of the Mississippi paddle steamers! Wherever are we going to get that?"

"I remember a story too," said Muffit. And his eyes shone as he told it. "Once, when I was in the Stars Department of Heaven, I looked out and watched you angels here in the Christmas Department. You were very worried about a little boy called Thomas, who spent a lot of time on his own. His parents kept a shop, and they didn't have much time for him. So when he wrote his letter he said, 'I want love for Christmas!' That was all, but it was giving you a lot of trouble here in the Christmas Department. You were all racking your brains! And on Christmas Eve, I could see you'd thought of something all right — because when present-giving time came, Thomas got a little dog. He was very, very pleased, and he even called his pet 'Love'. When he took the dog out for a walk, and called, 'Here, Love!' people used to turn and stare at him in surprise — but when they walked on again they were feeling rather better than before."

"And I know a story — an exciting one!" Noisy remembered. But suddenly he stopped, looking very surprised. "My goodness, Scatty, where *have* you been?" he asked.

There was Scatty, covered all over with wood shavings. He explained, looking rather silly, "Well, I was so tired I just fell into bed — but it can't have been my bed at all! It wasn't my bedroom either. It was the room where presents are packed up, and I must have got the doors muddled. 'Scuse me — I'd better go and tidy myself up!"

And off he went.

Christmas Cookery

How about some coconut macaroons? Most children like them, and they're easy to make. Here's a recipe for you.

Coconut Macaroons
You will need:
4 egg whites
200g/7oz caster sugar
200g/7oz desiccated coconut
grated peel of ½ lemon
Bake in a preheated oven at 150°C/300°F/gas mark 2.

Beat the egg whites until they are stiff (you can use an electric beater). They must make peaks firm enough to keep their shape if you tip the bowl. Gradually stir in first the sugar, then the desiccated coconut and then the grated lemon peel. With a teaspoon, put little heaps of the mixture on a buttered baking sheet. Bake the macaroons for 20 minutes, until done.

The Story of Muffit the Little Angel

12th December

Up in the Christmas Department of Heaven, Muffit was feeling much better. After all, everyone makes a mistake now and then, and the best thing to do is laugh at it — even if laughing at yourself isn't easy. And Noisy had made a splendid suggestion. "You come with me, Muffit!" he said. "You might like to play in our band. I play the drum," he added very proudly.

That sounded fun. Muffit and Noisy went into the music room, and Muffit was given a triangular piece of metal. "What's this for?" he asked, puzzled.

"It's a triangle," Noisy explained. "Here — you have this little stick too, and when I say 'Now!' you hit the triangle with it. Understand?"

Muffit nodded.

Other little angels sat around them, practising all sorts of different instruments. Suddenly silence fell. An angel with a stick in his hand was standing facing them.

"That's the conductor," whispered Noisy, "and the stick he's holding is his baton."

"One — two — recording!" said a mysterious voice in the background.

The conductor raised his baton and began waving it about in the air, and at the same moment all the little angels around Muffit started to play. Muffit felt hot and bothered. When was he supposed to hit his triangle? The conductor wasn't any help there!

So he simply hit the triangle whenever Noisy had banged his drum. It was quite hard work. At last the band stopped, and Muffit put his triangle down, with a sigh of relief.

Then the tune they had just been playing was played back to them, from a recording. ''Well done!'' said the conductor. ''That triangle sounds good, played together with the drum!''

Muffit was so pleased that he went quite red in the face.

Oh, How Merrily

1. Oh, how merrily, oh, how happily,
sing we praises to Christ our King!
When we were forlorn,
Jesus Christ was born.
Joyfully, joyfully let Christians sing!

2. Oh, how merrily, oh, how happily,
sing we praises to Christ our King!
Jesus came to earth.
Holy was his birth.
Joyfully, joyfully let Christians sing!

3. Oh, how merrily, oh, how happily,
sing we praises to Christ our King!
Angels in accord,
praise their heavenly Lord.
Joyfully, joyfully let Christians sing!

The Story of Muffit the Little Angel

13th December

The angels who had been playing music stopped for a rest. "Would you like me to show you how I played the triangle?" Muffit asked Noisy. "Look, I—"

But he was interrupted. Oops-a-daisy came dashing up and stumbled. "Oops-a-daisy!" he exclaimed, clutching Muffit to stop himself falling. And he didn't fall — but Muffit did, right into the drum! And the drum head burst!

Noisy started laughing, and he just couldn't stop. His laughter soon infected Muffit and Oops-a-daisy, and they were all laughing. But when at last Muffit clambered out of the drum, they soon stopped. Now they could see what a lot of damage had been done. They showed the conductor, feeling very much ashamed of themselves, and he was cross. "Really, can't you little angels be more careful?" he scolded them. "A drum like that is not a toy, you know! You must take it to the repairs room to be mended. And then go and make nuisances of yourselves somewhere else! I don't want you in here any more!"

The three little angels slunk away, feeling bad. That was what came of being so high-spirited! But after all, they hadn't done it on purpose — and now they wouldn't be allowed to play in the band any more. What a shame!

They were so cross that they took their temper out on the poor drum, handling it very roughly as they took it away.

The Story of Muffit the Little Angel

14th December

"All because of that silly drum!" said Oops-a-daisy crossly, and he kicked the drum so that it banged into the wall.

Suddenly Noisy stood still. "Oh, aren't we being stupid!" he said. "Fancy making such a fuss about a drum! Listen, and I'll tell you a story.

Once upon a time there was a dwarf called Sour. He had a neighbour whose name was Envy, and whenever those two dwarves met there was trouble. Each would accuse the other of stealing his stores of provisions laid in for the winter. Well, winter came, and the dwarves racked their brains to think of clever hiding places for their stores. And each kept watching the other, in case his neighbour had designs on his own provisions. In the end they dared not even visit their own stores to fetch food, just in case they were being watched, so of course Sour and Envy grew very thin.

At last spring came, and the snow melted. The stream near their two little houses rose and flooded its banks, carrying everything away. Sour and Envy were only just in time to save themselves by getting on the branch of a tree. Now what? At first they acted as if they hadn't even noticed each other. But it was rather cold. They took to looking at each other out of the corners of their eyes, and then they moved until they were sitting close together. It was much warmer that way. And they were so bored they told each other about the hiding places for their stores — well, the flood had carried the provisions off, anyhow! So Sour and Envy helped each other to pass the time, and when the water went down they were friends. Although of course they still quarrelled from time to time — after all, their names were Sour and Envy."

Christmas Cookery

Did you make our other biscuit recipes? If you did you're probably an expert biscuit maker by now. Here's another recipe to try.

Cinnamon Cookies
You will need:
300g/11oz flour
175g/6oz butter
80g/3oz sugar
½ teaspoon cinnamon
2 eggs and 1 extra yolk
2 extra tablespoons of butter
Preheat the oven to 180°C/350°F/gas mark 4.

Put all the ingredients except the last two tablespoons of butter on a board and work them together with your hands to make a dough. Chill it in the refrigerator for half an hour. Then roll it out thinly. Cut the biscuits into pretty shapes and put them on a buttered baking sheet. Now melt the extra butter in a small pan. Paint it over the biscuits with a pastry brush, and put them into the oven. They will be done after about 10 minutes. Enjoy them!

Christmas in the Mountains

Where do *you* usually spend Christmas? I expect the answer is probably, "At home with my family." Can you imagine what it would be like to go away and spend Christmas somewhere else, like Gavin, Kate and Steve in our story? You can read about the exciting things they did on the next few pages.

It was a Sunday not long before Christmas, and the big city was very quiet. People stayed at home, because it was raining, and no one wants to go out of doors in such miserable wet weather. There were Christmas decorations up in the streets, and Christmas trees outside many of the buildings, but you could hardly feel really Christmassy. The weather was all wrong!

Three children were looking out of a window at the rain. Their names were Gavin, Kate and Steve, and they were bored. That wasn't surprising, with everything so grey and wretched out of doors. They pressed their noses to the window panes and watched a few cars going by, throwing up thick sprays of water behind them.

Gavin was the eldest, then came Kate, and Steve was their little brother. Their mother came into the room. "Oh dear, can't you think of a game to play?" she said in a kind voice. "Have you written your letters to Father Christmas yet?"

"Oh, Mummy, it's no use trying to think of Christmas at the moment!" sighed Kate. "Christmas is supposed to be cold and bright and snowy, not wet like this!"

"It's a shame," Mother agreed. "But there's nothing to be done about it. I can't work a magic spell to make it snow, you know! But come along! I've made some hot chocolate, and we'll have chocolate and special Christmas biscuits and light the Advent candles. Then perhaps you'll feel a bit more Christmassy!"

At least it would be a change. The three children hurried to sit down at the table, and their father came out of his den too.

Mother poured the chocolate. The candles shone, and the freshly baked biscuits smelled delicious. Everyone felt a little better.

But Gavin complained to Father about the miserable weather too — maybe *he* would know how to make it snow? "Dad, isn't there any kind of invention for changing the weather?" he asked.

Father shook his head. "No, I'm glad to say there isn't!" he replied.

"Just imagine what it would be like if everyone could change the weather! We'd be in a terrible muddle. Somebody might want sunshine, and another person might insist on having rain for the garden, and meanwhile a third person would be making a thunderstorm come. A terrible thought! I'd even rather have a rainy Christmas!"

They were feeling more cheerful now, and Father thought of some more comical ideas about muddled-up weather. The children made a game of it, pretending stormy winds were blowing through their chocolate, and they were sunbathing in the light of the Advent candles.

They had quite forgotten the miserable weather outside.

Then Father mentioned it again. "But you'd really like to spend Christmas in the snow, wouldn't you?" he said.

"Yes, of course," sighed the children.

"But the weather forecast said there's going to be more rain," Steve added.

Father looked as if he had something important to say. "Well — suppose we went away somewhere there's sure to be snow?" he said.

"Where?" asked Steve.

"Up in the mountains with the Walter family, where we went for a holiday *after* Christmas last year!" said Father, smiling.

It was like having a bombshell dropped! "You mean we're going there again — and for Christmas itself?" "Oh, will we be spending Christmas with the Walters' children?" "When are we going?" "Can I take my skis with me?" So many questions rained down on Father that he had to put his hands over his ears, and when at last they died down he said with relief, "Right! Yesterday I had a letter from the Walters. It said their children are looking forward very much to seeing you, and yes, you must remember to take your skis, because there's a lot of snow in the mountains there already. And we start tomorrow morning."

What fun! They got out all their suitcases and packed them straight away, and next morning they all climbed into the car.

It was a long journey. They had to drive to a port, and cross the sea on a ferry, and then get in the car again and drive a long way. But as the road wound up into the mountains, Gavin said, "I saw a snowflake on the windscreen!" "So did I!" said Steve. "And there's another, and another — lots of snowflakes! It's snowing properly now!" They were driving into a beautiful winter landscape.

The children were beginning to feel tired after all that travelling, but the sight of the snow woke them up again.

"I want a snowball fight!" shouted Steve.

"That's not a bad idea," said Father. "It's time we stopped for a rest, anyway." So next time they came to a parking place he stopped the car. The children got out, and soon the snowballs were flying! There was another family parking there who had had the same idea, so of course Gavin, Kate and Steve joined in their game. It was lovely to have proper snow in their hands at last!

After a while the other family drove on. Mother had unpacked a picnic. They had sandwiches, and tea out of a thermos flask. When they started off again, the children's cheeks were pink and glowing.

Darkness fell quite early, and Father had to put the headlights on, but there wasn't much farther to go now.

At last they reached the little mountain village where they had been for a ski-ing holiday before. It looked the same as ever! The Walter family were looking out for them, and they all came to the door to welcome them in. The Walters had three children too, about the same ages as Gavin, Kate and Steve. There were two girls and a boy.

"So there you are!" said Mr Walter. "What sort of a journey did you have?"

"It snowed, and we had a snowball fight!" Steve told him, looking very excited.

They all shook hands. Then Mother said, "We'd better take our luggage straight to our rooms."

The Walters helped them carry the suitcases indoors. Gavin, Kate and Steve were sharing a room.

They went into their room and unpacked. Gavin and Kate put their things away in the big wardrobe.

But Steve couldn't be bothered to unpack. He had found the Walters' cat and took it into the bedroom to play with it.

"Come on, Steve, unpack your things!" Gavin told his brother.

"No," said Steve. "I haven't got time."

"What do you mean, you haven't got time?" said Gavin crossly. "Put that cat down and do a bit of work! We're supposed to be ready for supper in a minute!"

"But I have to look after this cat! She was pleased to see me — she needs me! You're just envious because she likes me better than you!" said Steve.

"Listen, there's Mummy calling!" Kate interrupted. "She wants us to go downstairs, so do stop quarrelling! We can finish putting things away after supper."

Steve put the cat down at once and rushed downstairs.

"Huh! He doesn't mind about cats so much when there's a meal in the offing!" muttered Gavin.

The children went into the Walters' comfortable living room. The table was laid for supper, and it smelled delicious. Gavin, Kate and Steve ate until they were full up. Then it was time to go to bed. One after another, the children went into the bathroom, and then slipped into their nice warm beds.

"Have a good sleep, and you'll wake up feeling well rested tomorrow!" said Mother. "And no more nonsense, mind!"

But as soon as she had closed the door behind her, pillows began flying. In the middle of the pillow fight, Steve slipped out of the room — and came back carrying the cat again. He took her back to bed with him.

"Honestly, this is too much!" said his big brother. He jumped out of his own bed and shooed the cat out of Steve's. She was frightened, and took refuge underneath the wardrobe.

"You don't have animals in bed with you!" said Gavin crossly. He was right, of course, but Steve was upset.

"I want the cat back!" he howled.

Meanwhile Kate was trying to lure the poor frightened animal out from under the wardrobe. "Come on, puss!" she called. But the cat wouldn't move. Gavin and Steve tried too. "Puss, puss!" they called, but the cat just hissed at them. Then Gavin got a ski stick and pushed her out, very carefully, so as not to hurt her. "Open the door!" he said. And the cat shot out on the landing and away.

Now the children really *were* tired, and they went straight off to sleep. Steve dreamed about a cat on skis.

At breakfast next morning, Father said, "I've heard that you can hire a horse sleigh in the village. Would you like a ride in a sleigh?"

"Oh, yes!" cried all the children.

Steve shouted loudest of all. "I want to hold the reins!"

A little later the sleigh drew up outside the house. The horse was snorting. Its breath came out like white clouds into the cold, wintry air. When Steve saw what a big horse it was he didn't feel quite so adventurous, and thought he would rather not hold the reins after all. He got in the sleigh with the others, and they all had a lovely ride. The Walter children came too, and they enjoyed it just as much as the others.

They went all round the mountain village in the sleigh. The children shouted for joy, so loud that you could hear them a long way off.

When they came back for dinner their eyes were shining. They had so much to talk about there was hardly time to eat!

"Who wants to go ski-ing after dinner?" asked Father.

"Me! Me!" everyone shouted eagerly. And not much more dinner was eaten after that, because the children were anxious to get out of doors with their ski boots on.

"Where are my gloves?" asked Kate, and Steve was wailing, "I can't do up this buckle on my boot! Help me, please, Gavin!"

Gavin was having trouble himself — the zip of his ski-ing trousers had stuck. But at last they were all ready. The Walter children were coming too. They all set off with Father. Steve ran on ahead. "The way to the ski lift is over there!" he called.

Back in the house, Mother heaved a sigh of relief. Now she could get the presents ready in peace and quiet. The children were so keen to go ski-ing they had almost forgotten it was Christmas Eve!

Mother and Mrs Walter carried lots of brightly coloured parcels into the living room, and soon it was looking very Christmassy.

Out on the mountainside, the children were enjoying themselves. Gavin and Kate were quite good at ski-ing, but last year Steve had been too little to ski much, so he still had to learn how. Father had said he could have proper ski-ing lessons, but Steve thought he wouldn't need them! He stood on top of a slope and started off. However, his skis slid towards each other and crossed — and Steve fell over in the snow.

He looked round in surprise. "Why won't these silly things go the right way?" he complained, struggling to his feet.

"Don't worry!" Gavin told him. "It was just the same for Kate and me when we started ski-ing. You'll soon learn!"

It was getting dark when the children came back from ski-ing. They leaned their skis up against the wall of the house and rushed indoors.

"I must tell Mummy what I've been doing!" said Steve. He tried to open the living room door, but he couldn't. It was locked! "What's going on?" he asked in surprise.

Then the children realized. "Oh — it's Christmas Eve!" said Kate. "We almost forgot."

"Is Father Christmas in there?" said Steve. He put his eye to the keyhole and tried to look through.

"Well, well — someone's feeling very inquisitive!" said Mother, coming downstairs. "How was the ski-ing?"

But Steve didn't mind so much about telling her now — he was longing to get into the living room and see if Father Christmas had been.

Mother wouldn't let him in yet, though. "You must go upstairs and take your wet ski-ing things off first, children," she said. "And then we'll see if that door is ready to open!"

The children ran upstairs as fast as they could, and changed their clothes in record time. Then they all hurried down again.

The Walter children were standing outside the living room door. They had had to change too. And they were all so excited, wanting to see what presents they would have!

But the living room door was still locked, so the children had to wait.

"Doesn't Father Christmas take ages?" said Steve. He was hopping impatiently from one foot to the other.

"Perhaps it's because he has to bring so many presents," suggested the Walter children.

"Yes, perhaps," said Steve. "I did send a very long list."
A little bell rang inside the room, the door opened, and the children went in, feeling very excited.

The first thing they saw was the big Christmas tree. The ceiling light had been switched off, and the room was lit only by the candles on the tree. The children felt rather solemn.

"Where are my presents?" asked Steve. He felt he couldn't wait — but he had to wait just a little longer, because Father got his guitar and played a Christmas carol on it, and Mother sang. The Walters joined in, and so did Gavin and Kate. Steve was the only one who was still looking round for his presents!

At last the moment to unpack the parcels arrived. The children thought this was the very best moment of the day. They had such lovely presents! They unpacked ski outfits, dolls, lovely books, building sets, and many, many other things. Steve had a stuffed toy cat. He would be allowed to take *that* to bed with him all right!

Mrs Walter had cooked a delicious meal, finishing with her special Christmas biscuits. Everyone felt very happy.

The children sat on the floor, playing with their new toys. Mother, Father and the Walters sat in chairs and talked. They might all have been one family, although the Walters lived in a little mountain village, and Gavin, Kate, Steve and their parents lived in a big city. But everyone enjoys Christmas just the same.

One of the Walter children, called Maria, had been given a recorder. She already knew how to play the recorder a little, and after several tries she managed to play "Silent Night" without making any mistakes. That gave the children another idea. They made themselves into a children's choir. And they sang carols to the accompaniment of Maria's recorder.

It sounded lovely. Their parents felt tears come to their eyes.

At last it was bedtime. The children went happily upstairs, and Steve cuddled his toy cat in his sleep.

The Story of Muffit the Little Angel

15th December

But meanwhile, what about Muffit the little Christmas angel? He and Noisy and Oops-a-daisy had been taking the drum off to the repairs room after they broke it, when last we heard of them.

Well, Muffit stayed there, hoping to find his friend Scatty. And he saw a heart-breaking sight! Lots of broken toys were lying about the room. He felt specially sorry for a teddy bear which had a big hole in its tummy. The bear was crying.

Sadly, he told Muffit his story. "I belonged to a boy called James, and once upon a time James loved me. But then he forgot about me and left me at the back of a cupboard. His friend Johnny found me there one day, and said he was sure I'd be a good parachute jumper. So the two boys tied me to an umbrella and threw me out of a top floor window — and that's all I know about it until I came back to my senses and found myself here! Oh, please make me into a nice bear again, and give me to a child who will love me more than James did!"

One of the other toys spoke up — Punch the puppet. "Teddy, James does love you really! I belong to James's friend Johnny, and Johnny told me how sad James has been since you had to go away from him and come here."

How happy the little bear was! "Oh, please mend me, quick!" he asked Muffit. "I want to go back to my James!"

"I don't know if I'm a very good mender," said Muffit uncertainly. But he was so sorry for the bear that he thought he must at least try.

So Muffit found needle and thread and began to sew. It wasn't easy — the bear's stuffing would keep spilling out again! But he did it, and he used big stitches that would show, so that James would never forget how he had hurt his faithful Teddy Bear.

The Story of Muffit the Little Angel

16th December

One of the dolls in the repairs room of the Christmas Department of Heaven had a nice story to tell Muffit.

"I belonged to a little girl whose father was a postman," she said. "One Christmas

Eve the father came home and told us he had met a very strange little girl that day. 'She was wearing torn trousers and a fur jacket,' he said. 'And she went up to a little house. I could see a man sitting at the window of the house, with his head in his hands. He looked very sad, and so did the seven children who were sitting around him.

But when that ragged little girl came in all the children suddenly cheered up, and the room didn't look a bit sad or gloomy any more. Then the little girl opened a cupboard.' The postman told us he had seen the family open it before, and he could have sworn it was empty. 'But the little girl took things out of it — a present for every child! Now the house was full of gladness — but the little girl had vanished, nobody knew where.'

My little mistress's father the postman wondered if that little girl could have been an Angel," the doll finished her story. "What do you think, Muffit?"

Christmas Decorations

Make a Spicy Circle!

Would you like to make spicy circles as decorations for the Christmas tree? They can look very pretty. To make a circle, you will need:

2 cardboard discs, each 5.5cm/2 inches in diameter
glue
50cm/20 inches of decorative red cord
dried grains or seeds from the kitchen cupboard, for instance dried peas, lentils, maize, rice, small pasta shapes, sunflower seeds, etc.

Choose one variety of your seeds or grains and stick them in a ring around the edge of one of the cardboard discs. Then choose another and stick another ring inside the first. Go on like this until you have completely covered the surface of the disc.

You can make all sorts of other patterns too. You could stick the grains in a star shape or in zigzag lines. See if you can invent a nice pattern of your own.

When both discs are covered, stick them together back to back. Now put some glue on the edges of the two discs and fit the cord around the outside — the picture shows you how. Tie a knot where the circle of cord meets. Now wait for the glue to dry. When it is dry, tie another knot at the top of the cord, and your decoration is ready to hang up.

Is it as pretty as the one in our picture? Maybe it's even prettier!

Every Year at Christmas

1. Every year at Christmas,
at that holy time,
down to Earth come Angels
'midst frost and rime.

2. Never seen by humans,
quiet as a mouse,
gliding with a blessing
into every house.

3. Coming to my own side,
showing me the way
I can be with Jesus
each and every day.

The Story of Muffit the Little Angel

17th December

Muffit the little angel was still in the repairs room of the Christmas Department of Heaven — and at last he found Scatty. Scatty was busy searching a box which was full of lots of bits and pieces of toy cars.

"Whatever are you doing?" asked Muffit.

"Well, I want to repair this toy lorry, but I can't find the pieces I need," said Scatty.

"Aren't there instructions telling you how to repair it?" asked Muffit.

"Yes, but I'm afraid I'm so scatterbrained I've lost them," Scatty confessed. "Oh well — we'll just have to manage without!"

The two angels set to work with a screwdriver and any spare parts they could find, but they couldn't get anywhere much with repairing the lorry.

"Oh, you two are hopeless!" said a voice. It belonged to an angel called Cleverclogs, who was good at repairing things. He put a few screws in, worked away for a minute or so — and there was the lorry, as good as new!

"So that's the way to do it!" said Scatty. "Now you've shown us how, we can do it too!" And he and Muffit set to work again.

"Don't!" shouted Cleverclogs — but too late! Muffit and Scatty had taken his nicely repaired lorry to bits again!

The Story of Muffit the Little Angel

18th December

Obviously Muffit wasn't much good at repairing toys — but there must be something he could do! He sighed, and set off again to see if he could find out what.

Out in the corridor, he heard a lot of sawing and hammering coming from behind another door. The noise of that hammering made him think Noisy must be in there — and sure enough, he was. The room was the carpentry workshop.

"Can I help you?" asked Muffit.

"Yes, do!" said Noisy. "Here — you can stick the legs on this table!"

Muffit took the pot of glue and stuck the legs on, very carefully. He waited for the glue to dry and then stood the table right way up.

"Oh dear — it wobbles!" he said. "One leg must be too long." He got a saw and shortened the leg. But the table still wobbled.

Perhaps I sawed too much off, he thought, so he shortened the other legs to match. But the table still wobbled! Muffit went on sawing away until the table didn't have any proper legs at all, just funny little stumps.

"Noisy, I think this table will need some new legs," he said.

Noisy looked at what he could be doing — and he could hardly believe his eyes!

"No, no, Muffit!" he said. "You have to stick the legs right at the corners of the table, and then it won't wobble. Here, I'll show you — it's easy when you know how!"

Christmas Cookery

Here's a quick recipe for a few more biscuits.

Nut Cookies
You will need:
2 egg whites
185g/6½oz sugar
a good pinch of cinnamon
125g/4oz ground hazelnuts
some small, thin wafer biscuits for the base of your cookies
Preheat the oven to 150°C/300°F/gas mark 2.

Put one third of the sugar in a bowl with the egg whites and beat until stiff, using an electric beater or rotary whisk. Then take a big spoon and carefully fold in the rest of the sugar, the cinnamon and the ground hazelnuts. Put the little wafers on a baking sheet, and pile small heaps of the nut mixture on top of them. Put the baking sheet in the oven and bake the cookies for about 35 minutes.

The wafers are important; they will keep the cookie mixture from running all over the place, and your cookies will end up soft and nice.

Santa Claus is
on his way

Christmas has come, with joy and mirth.
Deep snow has fallen down on Earth.
While up in Heaven, the angels make
Biscuits and sweets and Christmas cake.
They do not have a moment's leisure,
For they must give good children pleasure!
And by tomorrow, Christmas Day,
The goodies must be on their way.

Santa Claus puts on his good
Cloak, puts up his fur-lined hood,

And takes the donkey by the halter,
The little angels do not falter.

For they are going with him too,
With presents for me, presents for you!
Where *are* they going? Santa knows,
And they will go where Santa goes.

Old Santa Claus, as you can see,
Is carrying a Christmas tree.
And Punch the puppet's in the sack
Of toys upon the donkey's back.

Punch won't sit still. He jumps about,
And waves and smiles as he looks out.
He wishes *he* could have some fun!
He wishes he could dance and run!

"Miaow!" the kitten mews. "Miaow!
Stop shoving, Punch! Stop pushing, now!"
The donkey brays, "Hee-haw! Hee-haw!"
Look — the poor kitten hurts her paw
As she and Punch fall to the ground.
So there they sit, and all around

Are ice and snow and freezing wind!
Poor toys — they have been left behind.

But early in the woods next morning
Just as the light of day is dawning,
Two children, Ben and Jane, go out
To search the forest round about.
They want to help their mother, who
Needs wood to burn, and kindling too,
If she's to bake their Christmas pies.
The children can't believe their eyes!
"Look, Ben! Oh, look! A little cat,
And Punch the puppet, with his hat
And shoes of red, and at their feet
Are Christmas cookies, crisp and sweet!"
"Oh, children," mews the kitten, "do
Take me back home to stay with you!"

"Yes," says poor Punch. "Please, children dear!
For Santa Claus has left us here!"

"Oh yes!" the children cry. "We will!"
"Do come and stay," says Ben, "until
You find your proper homes again."
"We'll keep you warm," says little Jane.

But Santa Claus, no doubt you know,
Never forgets a toy, and so
He searches through his sack. Says he,
"Someone has gone! Who can it be?"
Next moment Santa Claus has guessed.
"It's Punch!" he says. "That little pest!"
"Hee-haw!" he hears the donkey bray,
"The kitten too has run away."

Poor Santa's face is full of care.
"Where can they be, I wonder — *where*?"

He cannot leave them in the lurch.
He sends an angel off to search.

She flies all through the woods — at last
She sees the children going past!

Taking the happy toys back home.
The angel need no longer roam!

She goes straight back to Santa, crying,
"Don't worry, Santa, I've come flying
To say the toys are safe and sound,
And to a nice, kind home are bound!
They are not freezing any more."
"Hee-haw!" the donkey brays. "Hee-haw!"

"Thank goodness," says kind Santa Claus,
"They're not still shivering out of doors!
Well, Ben and Jane can keep the kitten,
And Punch as well! I think I've written
That they're good children in my book.
Let's stop and have a little look.

Yes — so they'll get more presents too!
But hiding them I'll leave to you!"

By dead of night
The angels bright
Hide books and toys
For girls and boys.

The doll is meant for little Jane.
Her brother Ben will get the train.

"Santa loves children!"
Sings the bird.
A truer song
You never heard.

Santa leaves gifts for one and all —
At your house too he's sure to call.

The time is near
For Christmas cheer,
And candlelight
On Christmas night.

"The candles, and the
          Christmas tree!"
Cries Jane. "Oh, Ben,
          just come and see!
There's Punch — and look at
          Dolly dear!"
The kitten says,
          "I like it here!

The little angels came to say
That Santa's going to let us stay!
Look, Punch — it's time for them to fly!
Goodbye, dear angels, oh, goodbye!

It's nice and warm in here! Miaow!"
"Yes," Punch agrees with her, "and now

I'm very glad that we can stay!
Oh, what a happy Christmas Day!"

The Story of Muffit the Little Angel

19th December

Muffit and Noisy, the two little Christmas angels, were in the carpentry workshop of the Christmas Department of Heaven. They had just made a table together — and this one didn't wobble. "There," said Noisy. "Now, you paint the table while I make some chairs to go with it."

Muffit found some bright red paint. He thought children would like red, because it looks cheerful, and he began painting busily away. But once again he found that the job he was trying to do looked easier than it really was. Big drops of paint kept falling off the table top and trickling down the legs. Soon the table was in a terrible mess, and Muffit decided he had had enough! He threw his brush crossly into the paint-pot and made for the door — he was going to slip away on the quiet. But Noisy stopped him.

"No, Muffit!" he said. "It's no good running away when something doesn't work! We can always learn from our mistakes. Here — use this brush to get the extra paint off the table top and paint it evenly on the legs." And he added, "Please!"

Muffit, who had been hesitating, took the brush and went to work, even if he didn't feel very willing. But look — he managed to paint the table very nicely after all!

Then Noisy began to laugh. "Ha, ha, ha! It's only the table you were supposed to be painting, Muffit! I didn't tell you to paint yourself too! You look like an Easter egg. Ha, ha, ha!"

And he was laughing so much, and dancing about, that he fell into the paint pot. When he clambered out he was covered with red paint.

Now it was Muffit's turn to laugh. "Do you know what *you* look like!" he chuckled. "Like a little red devil! Ha, ha, ha! I'd rather look like

an Easter egg than a devil! Ha, ha, ha!'' And he went on laughing as poor Noisy stood up and looked at himself. He was red all over! The other little angels laughed too — and in the end Noisy had to join in too and laugh at himself.

The Story of Muffit the Little Angel

20th December

So now Muffit and Noisy both had to go off and wash and change. They had to scrub a great deal of red paint off themselves.

When at last they were clean again, Noisy said, "Now I must go back to the carpentry workshop. I haven't finished those chairs yet."

But Muffit thought he had done enough carpentry. He wondered where to go next, and as he was wondering he met Oops-a-daisy, who seemed to be looking for something.

"Oops-a-daisy!" he said, when he saw Muffit. "I'm looking for my cardboard boxes, Muffit. I was going to pack up some presents in them — I had them all ready, just a little while ago, but now they've disappeared. I can't find them anywhere."

"Who would want a lot of empty cardboard boxes?" said Muffit in surprise. He looked around — and then he noticed something.

"That's funny!" he said, pointing to the floor. There were red footprints on it! And he knew very well he had washed all the red paint off himself and his clothes and shoes. So who had been treading in the spilt red paint this time?

"I must find out where these tracks lead," said Muffit, and he followed them carefully. They led him to a room he had never seen before.

It's rather an odd feeling, standing outside a door into an unknown room. You wonder what's on the other side. Or Muffit did, anyway. He quietly opened the door, just a little way, and looked through the crack. There was no sound to be heard in the room, and he went in, cautiously.

There was his friend Scatty, so intent upon his work that he hadn't heard Muffit coming.

"Goodness me, Scatty, whatever are you doing?" said Muffit. "Those boxes come from the packing room — they're Oops-a-daisy's boxes! And now I know where the red footprints come from. I see you've got some wooden sticks there too — so you've been in the carpentry room!"

"Have I?" said Scatty in his scatterbrained way. "I suppose you may be right!" He put his scissors down and began gluing bits of the cardboard boxes together. He was making them into a little train. The wood sticks were axles for the wheels, which were made of cardboard.

"That's a nice train!" said Muffit admiringly. "The wheels go round, too! What made you think of it?"

"Oh, just seeing those cardboard boxes standing there," said Scatty. "Only now I've finished making my train, I don't know what to do with it."

Softly Falling, the Snow

1. Softly falling,
the snow covers the land below.
The lake and the wood are white.
Jesus is born tonight.

2. Grief and sorrow will flee.
Trouble no more we'll see.
Hearts will warm at the sight —
Jesus is born tonight.

3. Harken! the angel choir
sing, as they rise up higher
into the heavenly light,
"Jesus is born tonight."

The Story of Muffit the Little Angel

21st December

Muffit and Scatty, the two little Christmas angels, stood looking at the nice train Scatty had made and wondering what to do with it.

The door opened, and their friend Oops-a-daisy came in. He looked at Scatty's train too. Just like Muffit, he thought it was a lovely train.

"I know what!" he said. "You remember how I told you about that boy who wanted the Mississippi paddle steamer? Well, he had a bad accident last summer. He was run over by a car, and he was very ill. He's better now, but he still has to stay in a wheelchair, and it makes him feel sad when he sees other children playing. Perhaps Scatty's train would cheer him up? Can you draw the parts of it on flat sheets of cardboard, Scatty? Then it would be a model he could cut out and make for himself. It would be a nice way to help him pass the time."

Muffit looked at his friend in surprise. "You know, you didn't say 'Oops-a-daisy!' once!" he said.

Scatty took a piece of cardboard and began to draw — but he couldn't do it. He started again several times, but it was no good. He couldn't design the parts for the model. At last he put his pencil down. "I can't draw it!" he said. "Making it was easy, but I don't know just *how* I made it!"

"Let me have a go," said Muffit. "I was watching while you made the train."

And he began to draw. He filled sheet after sheet of cardboard!
The mouths of the other little angels dropped open in amazement.

300

The Story of Muffit the Little Angel

22nd December

"Muffit, you're a genius!" cried Oops-a-daisy. "You know what? You ought to be in the studio, painting!"

So Muffit went off to the studio — and he knew he had found the right place for him. He might be all thumbs, but not when it came to painting and drawing. He set to work painting the illustrations of picture books. Noisy had written a lot of stories for the books. Muffit read the stories, and then painted pictures for them.

This was one of his favourite stories.

A little creature called Liar had crept into the land of the dwarves. He was a very ugly little creature, with green hair, a long nose, and big ears like a donkey's. And whenever he persuaded a dwarf to tell a lie, his green hair grew thicker, his nose grew longer and his ears grew bigger. He was good at getting the dwarves to tell lies, and soon the land of the dwarves was full of quarrelling and suspicion. Liar was delighted, and rubbed his hands with glee.

But there was a dwarf called Honest, who saw what Liar was doing and decided to drive him away. You will be surprised to hear how Honest did it — he started telling lies himself! But he told such amazing, incredible lies that no one could believe them, and the dwarves just laughed. Soon they were laughing at all lies, whoever told them — and in the end they laughed at Liar himself.

That annoyed Liar so much that his legs shrank and shrank — and he ran away, only just in time, before they disappeared entirely.

O Come, Little Children

1. O come, little children, O come one and all,
O come to the manger in Bethlehem's stall,
and see what our Father in Heaven has done
to bring joy and gladness to everyone!

2. See how the sweet baby lies here by the light
of a small stable lantern, this wonderful night,
so fair and so blessed, so full of God's love,
more gracious than angels in Heaven above.

3. He lies here on straw, that most beautiful child,
watched over by Joseph and Mary so mild,
adored by the oxen, by shepherds and kings,
while above him, rejoicing, the angel choir sings.

GOTTSCHLICH

The Story of Muffit the Little Angel

23rd December

The last few days before Christmas simply flew! Muffit the little angel was very happy. At last he had found out what he was good at, and he painted picture books from morning to night.

"So there you are, Muffit!" said Noisy. Muffit waited for the door to slam — but it didn't. Noisy was being quite quiet today.

"Are you nearly ready?" Noisy went on. "Today's the day we send the presents down to Earth, and tomorrow is Christmas Eve." He looked at Muffit's pictures, and liked them. "I do like the way you've illustrated my stories!" he said. Muffit went quite pink with pleasure.

"Oops-a-daisy!" said Oops-a-daisy, coming along. "Come on, we must get to work. Will you pile all these parcels up at the gates of Heaven, please, Muffit and Scatty? That's an easy job — you can hardly do it wrong!"

Muffit and Scatty felt rather hurt, but they decided not to say anything. After all, they *were* rather apt to do things wrong! So they carried all the parcels off to the gates of Heaven and piled them up.

"Give me a hand, Muffit," said Scatty. "This parcel won't stand up straight."

The two of them gave the parcel a shove — and there was a tearing sound somewhere, but at last it stood up straight.

"There, Oops-a-daisy, we've finished!" they called. "Now what shall we do?"

Oops-a-daisy came hurrying up. His jaw dropped when he saw the pile of presents. "I told you to pile them up at the gates!" he said.

"Well, we did!" said Muffit and Scatty happily.

"But I meant OUTSIDE the gates, not INSIDE the gates!" groaned Oops-a-daisy. Muffit and Scatty looked at each other guiltily. Now they knew what that tearing noise had been — the handle of the gates of Heaven, bursting through the parcel's paper wrapping!

At Christmas Time

I hear a bell, I hear it ringing,
and angels far away are singing.
Dear children, do you hear them too?
Santa Claus will soon come to you!

St Peter, standing in the sky,
raises his keys to Heaven on high.
"Come, angels all, the time is near.
And Christmas comes but once a year!"

The angels shake their feather beds,
and snowflakes fall down on our heads.
For ice and snow and frost and rime,
are the best of weather at Christmas time!

Young Susie lies in bed a-dreaming
of Christmas candles bright and gleaming,
and dolls with plaits or curly hair,
doll's prams, toy dogs, a teddy bear —

And all the angels with pretty wings,
bringing her lots of other things.
The angels sing carols as they fly by,
hovering up in the starry sky.

And fairest of all in the golden light,
is the Christmas Angel, so lovely and bright!
The Angel nods at Susie, and smiles and beams —
then Susie wakes up, so goodbye dreams!

On winter evenings, after dark,
the little angels you may mark.
From house to house they fly about,
where children leave their letters out.

The letters come from girls and boys,
asking for presents: books and toys
and games, and model railways too,
and things to make and things to do.

Suppose the lake should freeze to ice,
a pair of skates would be rather nice!
And don't forget (the children write)
something to nibble on Christmas night!

The little angels, all day long,
are busy on the telephone.
"The Christmas Office on the line.
Toy Factory, please – ring one – two – nine!

We have some urgent orders, please.
I wonder if you couldn't squeeze
in one more toy delivery?
The children need so much, you see!

Games, toys and books, and all the rest –
and everything must be the best!
Ready for Christmas, yes. To be
delivered to the Christmas tree!"

The Christmas Angel sees the presents all
are ready waiting, great and small.
They must be counted, one by one —
there's something here for everyone.

Dolls of all shapes and sizes, pairs
of animals for Arks, and bears,
dogs, monkeys, puppets, a stork, a duck —
whoever gets them is in luck!

The shelves are crammed, the cupboards too!
Whatever will the angels do
for extra space? So many toys
waiting to go to girls and boys!

And up in Heaven the angels go
about their business: they stitch and sew,
they hammer and saw and cut and paint —
they work so hard they feel quite faint!

They make dolls, houses, cars, toy trains.
They take the most enormous pains
to see that each child gets the best
of presents, and they will not rest

Till Christmas Day comes, down on Earth,
that happy day of joy and mirth!
But till the dawn of Christmas Day,
the busy angels toil away.

They mix and cook and ice and make
many a tempting Christmas cake.
You scarcely would believe your eyes,
to see their biscuits and mince pies!

They stir the dough, they mix it well.
Is it all right? How can they tell?
An angel's finger is dipped in.
Yes — these will fill a biscuit tin!

Into the oven the biscuits go.
They come out crisp and brown. I know
that none of them will go to waste!
Wouldn't *you* like a little taste!

The bells ring out on Christmas Eve.
Time for our angel friends to leave!
And all the gifts are ready now,
packed into sacks, for that is how

They'll go down to the Earth tonight,
down past the stars, so clear and bright!
Fetch the toboggans, bring the sleighs,
to carry them down the starlit ways.

The angels' packing is soon done.
The trees are decked out, every one,
with tinsel and candles and balls of glass —
for down to Earth they too must pass.

Here's Mrs Sun, whose golden rays
warms Heaven even on winter days.
"Remember, little angels, please,
we do not want you all to freeze!

So put some good warm clothing on.
Your fur-trimmed jackets you must don.
It's cold, and you have far to go,
and Earth is covered up with snow!

Avoid the drifts, or else your toes
may freeze. And frostbite on the nose,
as you would find, is no more fun
for angels than for anyone!"

St Peter comes to Heaven's gate.
"The time has come, so don't be late!"
He takes his key and opens wide,
the doors, and off the angels ride

On rocking horses, scooters, skis,
skates, hobby-horses, as they please.
Seated in a star-spangled sleigh,
the Christmas Angel leads the way.

"Be careful," warns St Peter, "not
to take a tumble! You have got
toys to deliver safe and sound,
once you're all down upon the ground."

The angels do not hesitate.
They crowd out through the golden gate.
They skim past clouds, past moon and stars,
and planets – Saturn, Venus, Mars!

How happily they fly along!
How merrily they sing their song!
How cheerfully they carry sacks
and Christmas trees upon their backs!

Their robes and hair fly in the wind!
Has anyone been left behind?
No – and St Peter·stands on high
to wave the angel host goodbye.

At last they come to journey's end,
and now the little angels wend
their way through frost and ice and snow —
to human children they must go.

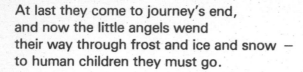

They search for paths, and country roads,
and set off with their festive loads.
The night is clear, the stars shine bright.
No village must be missed tonight.

Remote as cottages may lie,
they'll be discovered by and by.
The angels' blessing are for all —
men, women, children, great and small.

The Christmas bells ring out "Noel!"
Windows are opened, doors as well.
The angels, skimming over drifts,
fly in, delivering their gifts.

Look at your presents, children dear!
At last, at last your gifts are here!
The toys you've waited for so long!
"Noel," the bells ring out, "ding dong."

Delicious cooking smells arise.
Turkey and pudding and mince pies!
Make merry, laugh and sing and play,
for now at last it's Christmas Day!

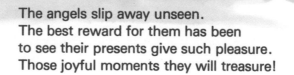

The angels slip away unseen.
The best reward for them has been
to see their presents give such pleasure.
Those joyful moments they will treasure!

The Christmas Angel, standing in the sleigh,
says, "You did very well today.
Not one tree nor one parcel lost,
despite the slippery ice and frost!

Follow me back to Heaven's gate.
For dear St Peter said he'd wait
to see us safely home, and old
as Peter is, he might catch cold!"

After their fun, there is no doubt
the little angels are worn out!
"Undress, and then it's off to bed!"
Yawning, they do as Peter said.

But down on Earth the happy boys
and girls are playing with new toys.
Feasting on apples, nuts and sweets,
all their delicious Christmas treats!

At evening, when the lamps are lit,
in warm, bright rooms the children sit.
They listen as the church bells chime,
and they rejoice at Christmas time.

Silent Night

1. Silent night, holy night,
   All is calm, all is bright
   Round yon Virgin mother and child,
   Holy infant so tender and mild,
   Sleep in heavenly peace,
   Sleep in heavenly peace.

2. Silent night, holy night,
   Shepherds quake at the sight;
   Glories stream from heaven afar,
   Heavenly hosts sing Alleluia;
   Christ, the Saviour, is born,
   Christ, the Saviour, is born.

3. Silent night, holy night,
   Son of God, love's pure light
   Radiant beams from thy holy face,
   With the dawn of redeeming grace,
   Jesus, Lord, at thy birth,
   Jesus, Lord, at thy birth,

Christmas Decorations

Straw Mobile

To make this amusing straw mobile, you will need:
15 straws of different lengths
16 wooden beads, each bead 0.5cm/about ¼ in diameter
string
a darning needle

Using the needle, thread your string through a bead. Make a good knot to keep the bead on the string. Now stick the needle through the middle of one of the straws and thread it on the string next to the wooden bead. Then add another bead. There is no need to make a knot this time. Add another straw, and then another bead, and so on until you have threaded all the beads and straws on to the string. Now your mobile is finished! The best place to hang it is over a heater, where it will begin to turn in the currents of warm air.

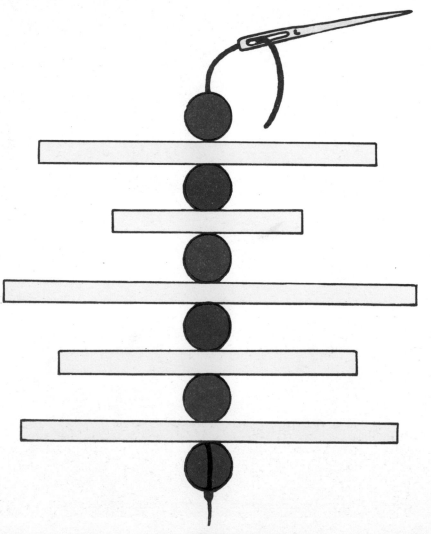

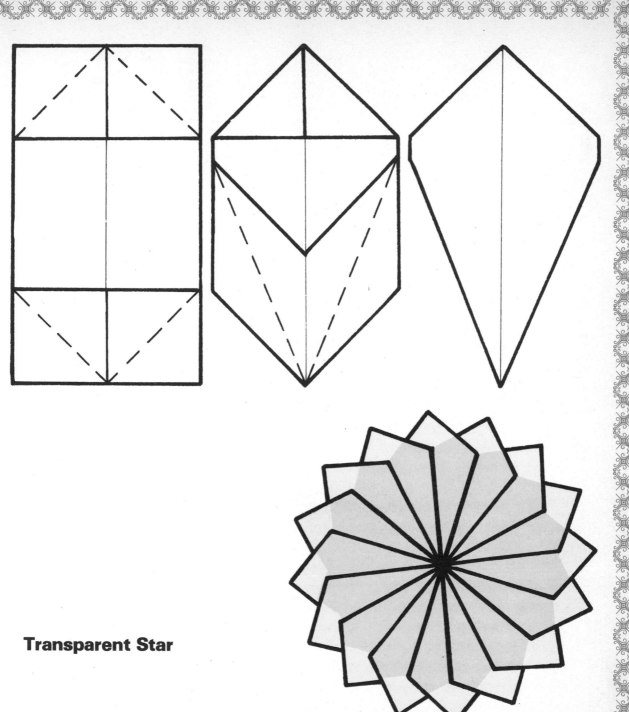

Transparent Star

You will need:
16 rectangles of transparent paper, each measuring 18 × 10cm/7 × 4 inches
scissors, glue, sellotape

Fold each rectangle once lengthwise and then open it out again. Now fold in all four corners to the central fold, and fold two of them again towards the centre (see diagram). Stick down the folded corners with sellotape. Stick all the sections together with glue as shown in the bottom picture. Now you can stick the star to a window pane.

The Story of Muffit the Little Angel

24th December

They were in trouble, up in the Christmas Department of Heaven. Muffit and Scatty, the two little angels, had piled up all the Christmas presents inside the gates instead of outside — and now the gates couldn't be opened.

"Let me have a go!" said Noisy. "After all, I'm good with doors."

He struggled through all the parcels, and began groping about. "I can't even find the handle!" he grumbled to himself.

Muffit and Scatty were feeling rather silly. They wouldn't meet anyone's eyes.

But at last Noisy managed to get the gates open — so now the little angels could load up the presents. It was high time, too! Santa wanted to set off down to Earth.

Muffit was rather thoughtful all of a sudden. "What happens to *us* now?" he asked.

"We get some sleep!" said Scatty, wearily.

"Yes, but after that! What about tomorrow?" Muffit said.

"Tomorrow we all go back to where we came from," said Noisy. "Our work in the Christmas Department is over."

"But that means I'll have to go back to the Stars Department!" said Muffit, a little sadly.

"That's nothing to complain of!" said Oops-a-daisy. "Somebody has to drop shooting stars to make people on Earth happy — and you're very good at dropping stars!"

"Anyway, Muffit, it's not so much fun here in the Christmas Department at other times of the year," said Noisy. "There's no excitement the rest of the time. And Christmas won't come again until next year. Perhaps you can come back then."

Yes — all was quiet now in the Christmas Department, and the little angels could rest after their hard work.

But there was one more thing they didn't mean to miss: they wanted to see the children getting their presents. After all, the little angels had worked away with so much love to make them! So they followed Santa down to Earth with their eyes.

They saw a little girl, reading one of the picture books made by Muffit and Noisy. Her eyes were shining. And the little boy in the wheelchair was delighted with the cut-out model of the train. He got to work with scissors and glue at once, and very soon he had made Scatty's train again.

And they saw little James, who was very pleased to have this teddy bear back, mended, and cuddled him lovingly.

And now Muffit himself was feeling very happy — for making others happy is the greatest pleasure of all.

Next night he was back in the Stars Department, hanging up the stars in the sky as usual. He was dropping some as usual, too.

The other day, however, something unusual and very exciting happened to Muffit. St Peter came to visit him in the Stars Department, and said, "You can come back to help us in the Christmas Department again next year if you like. How about it!"

And Muffit was so pleased that he dropped three stars at once.